Treasures

INTERACTIVE

Read-Aloud

ANTHOLOGY with PLAYS

Grade 3

Macmillan
McGraw-Hill

ACKNOWLEDGMENTS

"Give Me Normal" from PUT YOUR EYES UP HERE AND OTHER SCHOOL POEMS by Kalli Dakos. Copyright © 2003 by Kalli Dakos. Used by permission of Simon & Schuster Books for Young Readers, an imprint of Simon & Schuster Children's Publishing Division.

"Gratitude Is a Cool Attitude" by Jane Lanigan from Hopscotch, Dec./Jan. 2003, Vol. 14, Issue 4. Copyright © 2003 by Bluffton News Publishing. Used by permission of Bluffton News Publishing.

"If I Built a Village . . ." from IF I BUILT A VILLAGE… by Kazue Mizumura. Copyright © 1971 by Kazue Mizumura. Used by permission of Thomas Y. Crowell Co.

"Antarctica: Frozen Desert" by Elise Forier from Appleseeds, February 2003, Vol. 5, Issue 6. Copyright © 2003 by Cobblestone Publishing Inc. Used by permission of Cobblestone Publishing Inc.

"A Bear in the Family" by Ben Mikaelsen from Boys' Life, February 1997, Vol. 87, Issue 2. Copyright © 1997 by Boy Scouts of America. Used by permission of Boy Scouts of America.

"Move to the Beat" by Colin Hickey from Highlights for Children, September 2004, Vol. 59, Issue 9. Copyright © 2004 by Highlights for Children. Used by permission of Highlights for Children.

"The Wolves of Winter" by Rachel Buchholz from Boys' Life, February 1995, Vol. 85, Issue 2. Copyright © 1995 by Boy Scouts of America. Used by permission of Boy Scouts of America.

"The Sure-Footed Shoe Finder" from HERE'S WHAT YOU DO WHEN YOU CAN'T FIND YOUR SHOE by Andrea Perry. Copyright © 2003 by Andrea Perry. Used by permission of Atheneum.

"Galileo and the Moons of Jupiter" by Tony Helies from Highlights for Children, February 2002, Vol. 57, Issue 2. Copyright © 2002 by Highlights for Children. Used by permission of Highlights for Children.

"Writers" by Jean Little from INNER CHIMES: POEMS ON POETRY selected by Bobbye S. Goldstein. Copyright © 1992 by Bobbye S. Goldstein. Used by permission of Wordsong/Boyds Mills Press, Inc.

"Eating International" by Dee Murphy from Current Health 1, November 2003, Vol. 27, Issue 3. Copyright © 2003 by The Weekly Reader Corporation. Used by permission of The Weekly Reader Corporation.

"A Birthday Riddle" by Lana Renetzky from Highlights for Children, October 2004, Vol. 59. Copyright © 2004 by Highlights for Children. Used by permission of Highlights for Children.

"Walk Lightly" from A WORLD OF WONDERS by J. Patrick Lewis. Copyright © 2002 by J. Patrick Lewis. Used by permission of Dial Books for Young Readers, a division of Penguin Putnam Inc.

"From the Bellybutton of the Moon" from FROM THE BELLYBUTTON OF THE MOON by Francisco X. Alarcón. Copyright © 1998 by Francisco X. Alarcón. Used by permission of Children's Book Press.

Continued on page 222

B

CONTENTS

Unit 3

Unit 4

Unit 5

Plays

INTERACTIVE
Read-Aloud
ANTHOLOGY with PLAYS

Developing Listening Comprehension

Read Alouds help to build students' listening comprehension. This anthology offers selections from a variety of genres, including biography, fiction, folk tales, nonfiction, primary sources, songs, and poetry, to share with students. Instruction is provided with each selection to develop specific **comprehension strategies.** Students are asked to **set a purpose for listening,** as well as to **determine the author's purpose** for writing. Using the instruction provided, each Read Aloud becomes an enjoyable, purposeful learning experience.

What Makes a Read Aloud Interactive?

With each selection, **Teacher Think Alouds** are provided to help you model the use of comprehension strategies during reading. Using Think Alouds allows students to listen and to observe how a good reader uses strategies to get meaning from text. After reading, students are given the opportunity to apply the comprehension strategy. Students are asked to "think aloud" as they apply the strategy. By listening to a **Student Think Aloud** you can determine if the student is applying the comprehension strategy appropriately and with understanding.

Think-Aloud Copying Masters included in the Read-Aloud Anthology provide sentence starters to help students "think aloud" about a strategy.

Plays

Reader's Theater for Building Fluency

You can use the plays found at the back of this anthology to perform a Reader's Theater with children. Reading fluency is developed by repeated practice in reading text, especially when the reading is done orally. Reader's Theater can help build children's fluency skills because it engages them in a highly motivating activity that provides an opportunity to read—and reread—text orally. As children practice their assigned sections of the "script," they have multiple opportunities to increase their accuracy in word recognition and their rate of reading. Children are also strongly motivated to practice reading with appropriate phrasing and expression.

Performing Reader's Theater

• Assign speaking roles.

• Do not always assign the speaking role with the most text to the most fluent reader. Readers who need practice reading need ample opportunity to read.

• Have children rehearse by reading and rereading their lines over several days. In these rehearsals, allow time for teacher and peer feedback about pace, phrasing, and expression.

• Children do not memorize their lines, but rather read their lines from the script.

• No sets, costumes, or props are necessary.

GIVE ME NORMAL

by Kalli Dakos

Genre: Poem

Poetic Element: Imagery

Comprehension Strategy: Summarize

Think-Aloud Copying Master number 7

Before Reading

Genre: Tell students that some poems do not rhyme. These poems are called *free verse poems*. Explain that the poem you will read aloud is a free verse poem that tells a story. Like a story, it has characters, dialogue, setting, and a problem that may or may not be solved.

Expand Vocabulary: Introduce the following words and phrases before reading:

> *stovepipe hat:* a tall and skinny cylinder-shaped hat
>
> *patent leather:* a type of leather that has a shiny finish
>
> *normal:* the usual or expected way
>
> *in my book:* in my opinion

Set a Purpose for Reading: Invite students to listen to find out what the narrator in this poem considers normal.

During Reading

Read the poem's descriptions slowly and with expression to help students picture the scene in their minds. Read through the poem the first time without interruptions. Then reread, pausing to draw students' attention to the Think Aloud and genre note.

Give Me Normal

by Kalli Dakos

Ms. Roys met us
On the first day of school,
With a yellow <u>stovepipe hat</u>
On her head,
A skirt that stuck out
As if there were wires
Underneath it,
And black <u>patent leather</u> shoes
Like I wore in kindergarten.

She was waving
A bright yellow streamer,
And she yelled,
"Happy New Year, Penny"
As I walked
Into her classroom.[1]

"This is not <u>normal</u>,"
I thought to myself,
And sat down at
A bright red table.

Right over my head
Were dozens
Of giant inflated hands
Hanging from the ceiling.

Jennie leaned over
And whispered to me,
"She looks like something
Out of a fairy tale,
And what's with
All these hands?"

I started to bite
The nail on my baby finger,
Fairy tales, hanging hands,
And school
Don't go together
<u>In my book</u>.

Give me
Normal and regular
In a classroom
And I'm happy.
You can even give me
Boring,
As long as I know
What to expect.

But,
Don't give me
A fairy princess
In a Dr. Seuss hat,
Wearing kindergarten shoes,
In a class
With giant inflatable hands
On the first day of school.

That worries me.
That makes me bite my nails.

Think Aloud

[1]*This is mostly about a girl's first day of school and how she feels about her new teacher. I know this because the narrator of the poem tells me it is the first day of school. In the second stanza, Ms. Roys calls the narrator Penny.*

Genre Study

Poem: In this poem, the narrator repeatedly describes an unusual scene in her own words, summing up her thoughts in different ways. In the first stanza, she describes the teacher as wearing a stovepipe hat. Later, the hat is described as a Dr. Seuss hat. These details paint a vivid picture in the reader's mind of the new teacher and her classroom.

After Reading

Set a Purpose for Rereading: Once you have read aloud the poem for students' enjoyment, reread it for the purpose of having students identify the imagery and describing words.

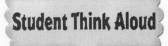
Student Think Aloud

Use Copying Master number 7 to prompt students to tell what the poem was mostly about.

"This was mostly about . . ."

Think and Respond

1. How would you feel if you walked into Ms. Roys's classroom on the first day of school? Why would you feel that way? *Responses will vary. Possible response: I would feel happy and excited because I enjoy surprises. I think Ms. Roys would be a fun teacher.* **Critical**

2. How would you describe Ms. Roys? What words does the narrator use to describe her? *Possible responses: Ms. Roys is wearing shiny leather shoes, a full skirt, a tall yellow hat and is waving a yellow streamer. The narrator uses the words* stovepipe, Dr. Seuss, princess, kindergarten shoes, *and* a skirt that stuck out. **Genre**

3. What does the poet tell us about the narrator of this poem? *Possible response: She tells us that the narrator doesn't like surprises, bites her nails when she is nervous, and likes it when she knows what will happen. She also tells us that the narrator's name is Penny.* **Author's Purpose**

Gratitude Is a Cool Attitude

by Jane Lanigan

Genre: Nonfiction Article

Comprehension Strategy: Analyze Text Structure

Think-Aloud Copying Master number 5

Before Reading

Genre: Tell students that you will be reading aloud a nonfiction article. Explain that this article presents information about a real person. It includes facts and details that will help readers learn more about this person.

Expand Vocabulary: Introduce the following words before reading:

> *gratitude:* being thankful
>
> *contribution:* a gift
>
> *stationery:* paper used to write a letter
>
> *campaign:* a special project

Set a Purpose for Reading: Invite students to listen to find out how a girl took a simple idea—saying "thank you"—and went on to write a book, create a Web site, and encourage others to show their gratitude in creative ways.

During Reading

Use the Think Alouds during the first reading of the text. Notes about the genre and multicultural perspectives may be used during subsequent readings.

Gratitude Is a Cool Attitude

by Jane Lanigan

"Hey, aren't you the thank-you kid?" A little boy in a Braves cap stops Ali at the mall. "I made a card for Mr. Walker, the crossing guard." Ali loves when people stop her to tell about their latest act of gratitude. She is proud to be known as the Thank-You Kid.[1]

How did Ali Spizman get her nickname? It all started when she was just five years old. Ali became CEO (Caring Executive Officer) of the pretend Thank-You Company. Her mom said, "Ali, why don't you point out kind people when we go places?"

Ali found caring people everywhere: the movies, the grocery store, school, the doctor's office. By the time Ali was 10, she had plenty of practice saying thanks. When her mother wrote a book for adults about writing thank-you notes, Ali decided she would do a cool version for kids.

Ali began collecting creative ways to say thank you. For over a year, Ali wrote a page a day. She also sent letters to important people. Ali always began her letters with a thank you for the special contribution that person had made; then she told them about her book and asked for a letter explaining why it was important to say thank you. Hillary Clinton, R.L. Stine, Disney president Michael Eisner, Mark Victor Hansen who wrote the *Chicken Soup for the Soul* books, and *Apollo 17* astronaut Eugene Cernan were a few who wrote back.

In 2003 *The Thank You Book for Kids* was published. In addition to the letters from her famous friends, Ali included hundreds of ideas that make writing thank you notes fun and easy. Begin with personalized stationery you make yourself using recycled greeting cards, art supplies, or the computer. Ali likes to make her cards into a frame by cutting out a small circle. She tapes a photograph of herself or the person she is writing to on the back.[2] Fruit becomes stationery when you use a permanent marker to write a message, such as "Orange you glad we are friends?" or "You are pearfect!" Other edible thank yous include: popcorn ("Glad you popped into my life."), crackers ("You crack me up."), and mints ("Mint for each other.").

Think Aloud

[1] *I wonder what it feels like to have people recognize you and stop you on the street. I think Ali likes it because she is proud to have people thinking about gratitude.*

Genre Study

Nonfiction Narrative: The writer uses sequence to tell the story of Ali Spizman. This is a commonly used text structure in nonfiction narrative.

Think Aloud

[2] *I notice that the writer mentions Ali's book in this paragraph. She makes the article more interesting by giving specific examples of creative thank yous from the book.*

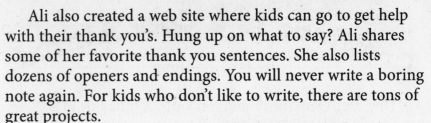

Ali also created a web site where kids can go to get help with their thank you's. Hung up on what to say? Ali shares some of her favorite thank you sentences. She also lists dozens of openers and endings. You will never write a boring note again. For kids who don't like to write, there are tons of great projects.

The Web site also tells about The Thank You Kid Campaign.[3] Ali started the campaign to help others say thanks and share best wishes. She asked children to donate different kinds of cards and notes to people who might not have any. Ali suggested making thank-you kits complete with cards, pens, and postage.

Kits could be dropped off at nursing homes, the hospital, or homeless shelters. Already, Ali has heard from Girl Scout troops, church groups, and children from all over the country who have joined the campaign.

Think Aloud

[3] This article makes me want to learn more about Ali and her special project. The writer included lots of interesting details.

After Reading

Retell: Have students tell three things they learned from the article. Have them give reasons they think these specific details are important.

Student Think Aloud

Use Copying Master number 5 to prompt students to share something they learned from the article.

"I noticed the author . . ."

Cultural Perspective

Have students discuss how gratitude or saying "thank you" is common to all cultures. In Japanese, there are three ways to say thank you, depending on how polite you want to be:

> *Domo arigato.* (polite)
>
> *Arigato gozaimasu.* (more polite)
>
> *Domo arigato gozaimasu.* (most polite)

Think and Respond

1. Why do you think it is important to show gratitude to others? *Possible responses: Saying thank you is a nice way to show others you appreciate them; showing gratitude makes people feel good.* **Inferential**

2. The writer presents events in the order in which they happened in Ali's life. What words and phrases help show sequence? *Possible responses: when she was five years old; by the time Ali was 10; for over a year; this year* **Genre**

3. Why do you think the author wrote this article? *Possible responses: The writer wanted people to learn about Ali and The Thank You Kid Campaign; the writer wanted to remind people that it is important to say thank you and show your appreciation.* **Author's Purpose**

IF I BUILT A VILLAGE...

by Kazue Mizumura

Genre: Poem

Poetic Element: Imagery

Comprehension Strategy: Visualize

Think-Aloud Copying Master number 3

Before Reading

Genre: Explain to students that some poems do not rhyme. Tell them that the poem you will read describes images of nature that show the poet's love of living things.

Expand Vocabulary: To help students visualize the details of the poem, introduce and explain the following words:

> *trout:* a type of fish
>
> *drifting:* moving
>
> *fiddleheads:* a type of green fern or plant
>
> *Northern Lights:* the name of beautiful lights seen in the sky above Earth's Northern Hemisphere

Set a Purpose for Reading: For the first reading, have students listen to and enjoy the descriptive language. Ask them to picture what the different animals would look like.

During Reading

Slowly read through the poem the first time without interruptions. Have students picture in their minds the scenes described in the poem. Then reread, pausing to draw students' attention to specific details. Use the notes about the genre during subsequent readings.

IF I BUILT A VILLAGE...

by Kazue Mizumura

If I built a village
Upon the hill
Along the river
In the woods,
There would be rabbits
Leaping in the sun,
Their white tails
A streak and a flash
Against the wind.

There would be <u>trout</u>
That shine like rainbows
Swimming in the river
As their shadows
Flicker and swirl
Through the ripples.

There would be owls, too,
For me to listen to when they hoot
In the woods at night,
Their eyes full of
Moon lights.

If I built a town
In the valleys
Around the lakes
Beside the forests,
I would leave the jumping mice
Sound asleep
In their nests,
Deep under the frosted valley,
Until the spring melts the ice.

And I would welcome the geese
From Canada

Think Aloud

I am able to picture in my mind the fish swimming in the river. The word rainbows *helps me picture light and colors. The words* flicker *and* swirl *help me imagine how the fish are moving in the water.*

Genre Study

Poem: Imagery includes the use of specific words that help the reader picture what the poet is describing. Describing words such as *jumping* and *frosted* help the reader imagine what the mice are doing and what the valley looks like.

As they line grandly
On the lake,
To glide in and out
Of the drifting mist.

I would keep quiet for the deer
Tasting the raindrops
Scattered from the fiddleheads
In the forest.

If I built a city
By the sea,
Beneath the ground,
High against the sky,
There would be whales' spouts
Fountain high,
Far out at sea
Sprinkling pearl sprays
Over the Northern Lights.

There would be moles
Seeking their meals along the
tunnels
Where the fallen leaves
Turn into earth
Soft and dark.

And there would be eagles
To soar to the sky
With their wings
Spread and still
Amid the summer clouds
As long as they wished.

If I built my village,
My town and my city—
There would be people
Who would care and share
With all living things
The land they love.

After Reading

Set a Purpose for Rereading: Have students listen for specific nouns and adjectives that help them picture details in the poem. Discuss the language of the poem with the students. Have students identify how the language makes them feel or how it appealed to their senses.

Student Think Aloud

Use Copying Master number 3 to prompt students to identify a specific place described in the poem.

"I was able to picture in my mind . . ."

Think and Respond

1. How would you describe the village the writer would like to build? *Possible responses: The village would be a beautiful place with many animals; people and animals would live together.* **Critical**

2. Think about the details the poet uses to describe the village. Identify some specific examples that helped you picture it in your mind. *Possible responses: hill, river, woods, rabbits, white tails, rainbows, jumping mice, frosted valley, mist, pearl sprays* **Genre/Imagery**

3. What message do you think the poet wanted to share? *Possible response: She wanted to show the beauty of nature and remind people that we share the world with animals.* **Author's Purpose**

Antarctica: Frozen Desert

by Elise Forier

Genre: Nonfiction Article

Comprehension Strategy: Summarize

Think-Aloud Copying Master number 7

Before Reading

Genre: Explain to students that you will be reading aloud a nonfiction article about the continent of Antarctica. Remind them that the writer presents facts and includes descriptions to help them better understand the information.

Expand Vocabulary: To help students better understand the article, introduce the following words before reading:

continent: a large area of land

harsh: hard, difficult

marine: something that lives in the sea

extinct: a group of animals that are no longer alive

Set a Purpose for Reading: Invite students to listen to find out why the title calls Antarctica a frozen desert.

During Reading

Use the Think Alouds to help students understand the details provided by the article. Notes about the genre and cultural perspectives may be used during subsequent readings.

Antarctica: Frozen Desert

by Elise Forier

Antarctica is the coldest, windiest, driest place on Earth, covered by thick sheets of blue-white ice and surrounded by fierce, freezing seas.

More than 2,000 years ago, early Greek geographers wrote about a giant <u>continent</u> at the bottom of the world. Although no one had actually seen it, they called it *Anti-Arktikos*, or "opposite of the Arctic." Centuries passed, and no one found this "great southern continent." In the 1800s, explorers finally reached the legendary land. Among them was American sea captain Nathaniel Palmer, who sighted Antarctica from his ship.

Most of Antarctica is a desert. This may seem strange, because we often think of deserts as hot places filled with sand. Almost all of Antarctica is covered with snow and ice, and the average annual temperature is far below freezing. But on the whole, Antarctica receives very little precipitation (rain or snow)—and this is what makes it a desert.[1]

Plants and animals that live in Antarctica have to be tough. A few kinds of plants—some mosses, for example—grow in the 2 percent of Antarctic land that is free of ice. Some grow only during the summer months and only on the warmer parts of the continent. Animals that survive year-round on the mainland are small and stay close to the ground—tiny insects such as mites, and microscopic worms. (Penguins and seals live on Antarctica only part of the year—during breeding seasons.)

Some early visitors to the continent were hunters. Although Antarctica is a <u>harsh</u>, nearly empty land, the seas surrounding it are rich with <u>marine</u> life. Six species of seals, more than 12 species of birds—including penguins—and many whales live and breed near Antarctica. (Penguins and seals breed on the continent, its islands, and the ice that surrounds some parts of it.) Throughout the 1800s, whale and seal hunters sailed to the Antarctic oceans by the hundreds. The hunters sold sealskins and whale and penguin blubber. (Blubber is the thick layer of fat below the skin of marine animals.) So many seals were killed that several species almost became <u>extinct</u>. Today, Antarctic seals are protected by international agreement, and their populations have increased again.

Think Aloud

[1] *This paragraph is mostly about why Antarctica is a "frozen desert." I learned that a desert isn't necessarily a place that is hot. Any place that receives very little rain or snow is called a desert.*

Think Aloud

[2] At first I thought Antarctica was one giant block of ice where no people or animals can live and no plants can grow. Then I found out that many people live and work in Antarctica to study what this place is like!

Genre Study

Nonfiction Article:
I notice that the author uses facts and numbers to give information about the topic. She tells about the number of species of seals and birds. The author also gives the definitions of certain words.

Other people to visit Antarctica included explorers, scientists, and adventurers. Explorers rushed to claim pieces of Antarctica for their nations. In the interests of preserving the land and avoiding war, the international Antarctic Treaty was signed in 1959. It ensures that Antarctica will remain a peaceful place and will be protected from harmful activities.

More than 3,000 people from around the world—scientists and people who help the scientists—work in Antarctica today.[2] It is not a very easy place to live, but it is a perfect laboratory for scientific study. Astronomers like the cold, clean, dry air because it allows their telescopes to see clearly into deep space. Biologists study life on and around Antarctica to learn about how animals and plants adapt to extreme temperatures and harsh conditions. Geologists dig in Antarctica to find out what the land was like millions of years ago. Glaciologists (scientists who study the great masses of ice called glaciers) drill in the ice to trace climate changes throughout the ages. Some scientists study animals and plants on Antarctica to find out more about what life might be like on other planets.

With its huge icebergs, blue and silver landscape, whistling winds, and chilly seas, Antarctica can seem like another planet. The land and its icy cover have been compared with the Moon, Mars, and Jupiter's moon, Europa. Possibly no place on Earth is stranger or wilder—or more beautiful—than Antarctica. Certainly, there is no other place we know of that is quite like it.

After Reading

Summarize: Have students tell what they think the article was mostly about.

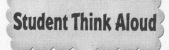

Use Copying Master number 7 to prompt students to summarize what they learned.

"This was mostly about . . ."

Cultural Perspective

On December 14, 1911, explorer Roald Amundsen of Norway became the first person to reach the South Pole. Since that time, explorers from many other countries have journeyed into Antarctica. Expand this idea by asking students to discuss the theme of exploration in literature across times and cultures.

Think and Respond

1. If Antarctica is the "coldest, windiest, driest place on Earth," why do so many scientists want to study there? *Possible responses: The clean air makes it easier to see into space; biologists go there to learn how plants and animals can survive in such a cold place.* **Critical**

2. The description of Antarctica in the first sentence makes it seem like a place where nothing could live and no one would want to go. How does the article show that this is not true? *Possible responses: We learn that for hundreds of years people have wanted to explore Antarctica; we also find out that plants, animals, and people can live there.* **Genre**

3. Why do you think the author chose to write about Antarctica? *Accept reasonable responses. Possible responses may include the fact that she finds Antarctica interesting, or perhaps she wanted to share what she had learned with others.* **Author's Purpose**

A Bear in the Family
by Ben Mikaelsen

Genre: Nonfiction Narrative

Comprehension Strategy: Generate Questions

Think-Aloud Copying Master number 1

Before Reading

Genre: Explain to students that a nonfiction narrative features real people and real events. In this selection, the writer describes something that actually happened to him.

Expand Vocabulary: Introduce the following words to help students better understand the narrative:

> *nuisance:* something that annoys or bothers you
>
> *bruin:* another name for "bear"
>
> *cower:* to shake with fear
>
> *den:* an area that an animal sleeps in

Set a Purpose for Reading: Have students listen for how the author feels about having a bear for a pet.

During Reading

Use the Think Alouds during the first reading of the text. Notes about the genre may be used during subsequent readings.

A Bear in the Family
by Ben Mikaelsen

A neglected dog becomes a 40-pound nuisance. A neglected bear can kill you. Thankfully, the author's pet bruin, Buffy, is anything but neglected.

I was stopped once for speeding in my pickup truck. As the highway patrol officer wrote me a ticket, our pet, Buffy, poked his head out the open window, grabbed the ticket pad from the officer's hand and ate it.[1]

The officer stared, speechless, then drove away and totally forgot my citation.

You would too. Buffy is a 7-foot, 600-pound black *bear*.

Bringing Baby Home

Thirteen years ago my wife and I adopted Buffy. A research facility that had been studying him returned him to the game farm where he had been born.

Melanie and I knew little about Buffy's past except that he could not go to a zoo or be freed to the wild because his claws had been removed (we don't know why). And we knew he'd probably be treated as a useless animal—and therefore killed—if left on the farm.

So we agreed to take the 20-pound, 16-week-old cub to our Montana home.

Before picking up our new baby, we read dozens of books on bears and got the state and federal licenses required to keep the animal. We spent $25,000 to build a sturdy chain-link pen around two sides of our house. We made Buffy a spring-fed pond, a playground and a den and gave him plenty of running room.

Finally, we were ready for anything—we thought.

Raising a Rascal

The cuddly rascal who suddenly joined our family (which also includes four cats and a dog) caught us unprepared.

The first night, I lay in bed listening to his haunting cry. I crept out and sat near him in his den. After a few minutes he crawled onto my lap and sucked the pads on his front feet. I hummed and rocked him to sleep.

Think Aloud

[1] *I notice the author begins with an interesting event. It grabs my attention and makes me want to read more.*

Genre Study

Nonfiction Narrative: The writer uses subheads to break up the story. Subheads are like headlines in a newspaper. They capture the reader's interest and give an idea of what the next section of the story will be about.

The first six months, I rocked Buffy to sleep every night. I spent hours feeding him, playing with him, watching him. Every sound or gesture puzzled me.

Because Buffy's muscle structure and coordination resembles that of a human, his play is very human-like. Mentally, we find him much harder to figure out. As a mere 100-pound cub, he would stand and shake his head playfully at a neighbor's angry Angus bull. Other times he would cower behind me at the sight of a small lamb.

And he is so mischievous. One day Buffy, then 6 years old and 400 pounds, sneaked into the house while we were gone. For an hour he sat in our bathtub, tearing down the shower curtains and biting open every bottle of shampoo and conditioner he could find. He even turned on the water and smeared some toothpaste in his armpits and on the ceiling.[2]

What a mess! But he was so proud of himself, I had to hug him.

Watch Out for That . . . Tongue!

When we first got Buffy, he nursed from a bottle. When I tried to wean him at 5 months old, he refused solid foods. Melanie solved that problem by substituting his bottled milk with water.

Buffy took one suck and angrily threw the bottle across the kitchen. Then he ran after it and sucked again. A second time he flung it. By that night he had abandoned his beloved bottle and ate solid food.

Many things about Buffy we learned the hard way. I never appreciated how long his anteater-like tongue was until we were playing one day when he was still a cub.

With a piece of candy in my mouth, I blew gently into Buffy's face to watch his nose twitch. In a blink, Buffy snaked his long tongue to the very back of my throat. He licked my tonsils and stole the candy. While I gagged, my wife howled, laughing.

Finally, a Bond Develops

Our friendship with Buffy grew painfully slowly. But one evening, I discovered a wild male black bear attacking Buffy's pen. The wild bear had nearly broken down the door. I shouted and threw rocks until the bear lumbered off, then I crawled in the pen.

Buffy's tiny front feet—he was only about 5 months old at the time—pumped out from under his fuzzy rump as he ran frantically in circles, bawling with fear. Finally he stopped and stared at me. Shaking, he clambered onto my lap and hugged me. I was crying. We cuddled for a long time that night.

Finally we slept the night together, bonding and becoming family. Overnight I became not only his provider, but his guardian.

Wild Animals Are Not Pets

I do not recommend wild animals as pets. Dozens of times I have seen tragic results with someone hurt or killed. A neglected dog becomes a 40-pound nuisance. A neglected bear can kill you. That said, Buffy has learned that I exist to help him.

I spend three or four hours each day with him. He trusts me so much he has bitten down on his own forearm while I cut open his paw to remove a sliver.

Buffy's play can be funny. When he teases the dog, he avoids a nip on the nose by going over to the closet and bringing back a broom to use as a poke stick.

He can also be scary. Last summer, Buffy stood behind me and wrapped his huge forearms around my arms and chest. When I told him to get down, he laid back his ears and squeezed harder. I stomped on his hind toe. He bawled and grabbed the hurt toe, dancing in circles on the other hind foot. Then, standing at his full height, he roared in my face.

His humid breath fogged my glasses as we stared at each other for several tense seconds. Then he sat and rubbed his toe. I kneeled next to him and helped rub his hurt paw. Soon he nuzzled my nose, his gesture of forgiveness.

I've learned that Buffy has a keen sense of justice. If a stranger had stomped on his toe for no apparent reason, Buffy would have killed him.

Guarding Buffy

Most summer afternoons we hike in the woods or go swimming. Buffy loves to run free, eating berries, overturning rocks and tearing apart rotted stumps to look for grubs and ants. Because of hunters, we do not wander far apart. Buffy now believes that all people are to be trusted. Sadly, this is not true.

The hunting of bears in Montana makes many cubs orphans. The cubs die slowly from starvation. That's why I wrote my first novel, "Rescue Josh McGuire," a story about a boy trying to save a bear cub's life. Luckily, Buffy will never be hunted.

Time to Sleep, Bear

During winter, heavy snows cover the ground here in Montana. To keep from starving, all bears sleep until spring.

As the autumn air cools, Buffy grows thick hair. His compulsive eating adds body fat from which he draws energy during his six months of hibernation.

Before hibernating in his straw-filled den, Buffy collects all his toys: a basketball, a tire, a skateboard and a big food dish. He sets these carefully around his nest.[3] Then, protected from the icy winter wind and snow, he settles in for his nap.

Melanie and I crawl into the darkness of his den for a short good-bye. If we stay too long, Buffy pulls straw over our legs as if preparing us to stay.

Hibernation is a part of Buffy's world we cannot share. We wait until he is sound asleep before leaving. We'll miss him while he naps, but next spring our lives with Buffy will pick up where we left off.

With a hug.

Think Aloud

[3] When I read about Buffy collecting his toys, it reminds me of a child. Now that I think about it, the writer tells about many ways he treated the bear like a human baby. He rocked the bear to sleep, gave Buffy a bottle, and comforted Buffy when he was scared by the wild bear.

Take Notes: Have students write what they learned about having a bear as a pet. Invite them to share their notes and opinions about the selection with each other.

Student Think Aloud

Use Copying Master number 1 to help students share something from the story that they would like to learn more about.

"I wonder . . ."

Think and Respond

1. How does the author show that wild animals should not be pets? *Possible response: He tells about his own somewhat dangerous experiences with a bear.* **Critical**

2. How can you tell this selection is nonfiction? *Accept reasonable responses.* **Genre**

3. What message do you think Ben Mikaelsen wanted to share with his readers? *Possible responses: The writer had many difficulties raising a bear in his home, but he had a special bond with Buffy. Buffy was hard to live with sometimes, but the writer loves the bear like his own child.* **Author's Purpose**

Move to the Beat

from *Highlights for Children*

by Colin Hickey

Genre: Expository Text

Comprehension Strategy: Generate Questions

Think-Aloud Copying Master number 1

 ## Before Reading

Genre: Tell students that an expository text such as the one you will read aloud tells about a specific topic. Explain that they will listen to an informational text about a musician from Africa. Jordan Benissan is a master drummer who teaches American children about the music of his homeland.

Expand Vocabulary: Introduce the following words before reading:

>   *master:* someone who is highly skilled in a special area

>   *mimic:* to imitate or copy

>   *uplifts:* raises one's spirit

>   *accompanies:* goes along with

Set a Purpose for Reading: Invite students to listen to find out about Jordan Benissan and what makes this text informational.

 ## During Reading

Use the comprehension Think Alouds during the first reading of the story. Notes about the genre and cultural connections may be used during subsequent readings.

Move to the Beat

from *Highlights for Children*
by Colin Hickey

Jordan Messan Benissan starts by drumming. He strikes the drums with his hands, sometimes in the center, sometimes on the side, sometimes with a quick brush of the surface.

Before long Benissan, a <u>master</u> musician from the West African country of Togo, has his audience of schoolchildren tapping their feet to the pattern of his drumming. Then he tells them to clap with the pattern. They do, and the music gets louder.

Next Benissan begins to sing. "Gun, godo, pata. Gun, godo, pata. Gun, godo, pata," he chants. His words <u>mimic</u> the sounds he creates when he hits the drums in various ways.[1] The words, the claps, and the drumming all fit together, all move to the same beat.

Get Up and Dance

"Rhythm helps you hear music and feel music in a very different way," Benissan says. "So it <u>uplifts</u> you and really awakens your soul to it. From that it becomes very physical. It takes over your body, and that's why it makes you want to dance to it. That's how it happens."

By this point most students are clapping, singing, and dancing to the music. This is how Benissan teaches kids in the United States about the music of his country. It works every time.

Music serves an important role in Togo, a country of more than five million people. A master musician in Togo is a performer, a teacher, a historian, a healer, and a voice for the community. The people of Togo use music to understand and connect to the past, back to the first master musicians centuries ago.

"When you read about history, it is not the same as when it is told to you with a human voice, because the book doesn't have the warmth of the human voice," Benissan says. "That is the best part of the tradition. When things are told to you, you feel the warmth."[2]

Think Aloud

[1] *The words to the song help me hear the rhythm of the drums. I want to know how important music is in Togo. I'll keep reading to find out.*

Think Aloud

[2] *The writer describes how the people of Togo use music to get in touch with their past. From the description, I can see that music must be passed down from generation to generation.*

Think Aloud

[3] *I wonder what it is like to hear music in your head whenever you are doing something, like preparing dinner or washing the dishes.*

Everyday Music

Not everyone in Togo can be a master musician like Benissan, but most Togolese also make music a part of everyday life.

"My parents," he says, "were not professional musicians, but they would dance and sing." They took a very active part in making music.

This is the way of Togo. Even everyday chores are often done with music in mind. When a carpenter swings his hammer, he might swing the tool in a pattern that produces rhythm. When an office worker types a letter, the clacking of the keyboard can become a performance.[3]

When there is a community project to accomplish, such as building a school or a church, people throughout the community join forces. They come not just with tools but with instruments and songs so that music accompanies the work and provides a pattern—a harmony—to the task.

A Family of Drums

Benissan uses drums of many shapes and sizes when he plays. Those different drums, he says, form a family. His drum family has a father, a mother, an older brother, a daughter, twins, and a baby brother. In Togo, people add a bell and a shaker to the drum family. These instruments, Benissan says, give music its heartbeat.

When the drum family works together combining its different sounds, it produces a composition more beautiful than any one instrument could produce alone. Benissan believes that the same principle applies to people.

"As a member of a community in Africa, everybody is very important," he says. "Whether you are small or big, your contribution is important, very valuable to the whole group effort."

Day or night, Benissan can be found playing his drums, putting different rhythms together or pulling them apart to fit them together into a new pattern. But his greatest joy comes when he takes his drums into a school. Children clap, dance, and sing, moving to the beat of his music. Together, the master musician and the students create something even more beautiful.

Summerize: Have students summerize the selection. Review and discuss how the details reinforce the information provided.

Student Think Aloud

"I wonder..."

Use Copying Master number 1 to prompt students to share a question they have about Jordan Benissan, his music, or the country of Togo.

Cultural Perspective

Jordan Benissan is a member of the Ewe people from Togo in West Africa. Have students identify the cultural elements of the story and then compare and contrast Benissan's life as a musician with that of an American musician they know.

Think and Respond

1. Name some common activities that involve music in Togo but not in our culture. *Possible responses: Music is part of everyday life and common activities sush as hammering or typing. Musicians provide live music at construction sites.* **Analytical**

2. The selection starts with a description of how Jordan Benissan performs. Why do you think the text begins that way? *Possible response: The description is very lively and helps you picture Benissan and the way he plays and sings. This is really important since the whole selection is about the musician and how he performs.* **Genre**

3. Why do you think Colin Hickey wrote this article? *Accept reasonable responses. Possible responses: Perhaps he wanted to share the importance of music with others.* **Author's Purpose**

THE WOLVES OF WINTER
by Rachel Buchholz

Genre: Nonfiction Article

Comprehension Strategy: Analyze Text Structure

Think-Aloud Copying Master number 5

Before Reading

Genre: Tell students you will read aloud a nonfiction article about a man who takes photographs of wolves in the wild. Remind students that the purpose of this type of text is to inform, or present information about a specific topic.

Expand Vocabulary: Introduce the following words to help students understand the article:

> *cull:* to reduce the size of a herd by killing weak or sick animals
>
> *prey:* an animal hunted by a predator for food
>
> *startled:* frightened
>
> *peek:* to look at or into

Set a Purpose for Reading: Invite students to listen to the article to learn about how wolves behave in the wild.

During Reading

Use the comprehension Think Alouds during the first reading of the story. Notes about the genre and cultural perspectives may be used during subsequent readings.

THE WOLVES OF WINTER

by Rachel Buchholz

Snowshoeing across a frozen lake in Minnesota, photographer Jim Brandenburg couldn't believe his eyes. Trotting straight toward him was a gray *wolf*.

Brandenburg dropped to the ice, aimed his camera—and waited. Did the wolf see him? Yes. It advanced slowly toward the funny-looking lump on the ground.

"Maybe it's a dead moose for dinner," the wolf may have been thinking.

Suddenly, the wolf stopped, realizing that Jim was human. The animal seemed embarrassed.

"The wolf simply walked away," Jim said. "He looked at me over his shoulder once like, 'Oh, no! I can't believe it!'"[1]

Brandenburg was sorry to see the wolf go, but not surprised. After 25 years of photographing wolves, he knows they are shy around people.

BIG, BAD WOLF

As a boy, Jim held the common view that *wolves* are bad. But by reading and observing, he learned that they are a valuable part of the wilderness. They <u>cull</u> weak and sick animals and help preserve the balance of nature.

Wolves may fiercely hunt deer, elk and other <u>prey</u>, but they would rather run away than face a human. (Like all wild animals, they should be treated with respect and caution.)

To keep from scaring the wolves, Jim moves slowly when photographing them. He watches their actions to see if they've been <u>startled</u>. He avoids eye contact and pretends to ignore them.

"You kind of have to pretend you're a cow munching on some grass," he says.

WOLVES ARE SMART

Wolves belong to packs, as we belong to families. A pack usually has a mother, father and three to six offspring that hunt and play together. Each pack considers a certain area its territory—and will protect it against other wolves.

Think Aloud

[1] *I noticed the author wants to show us that wolves are shy. I wonder why the author did this?*

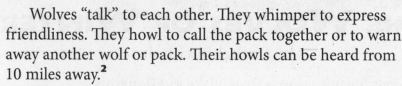

Think Aloud

[2] The author presents some interesting facts about wolves. I had no idea a wolf's howl could be heard ten miles away. Do members of a pack even get so far from each other?

Wolves "talk" to each other. They whimper to express friendliness. They howl to call the pack together or to warn away another wolf or pack. Their howls can be heard from 10 miles away.[2]

Wolves are clever hiders.

"Many times I'll be in the woods," Brandenburg says, "and I'll know that a wolf is there—I'll either hear it or see its tracks—but I'll never see it." So Jim has had to be clever, too.

He started by building a cabin in wolf country, the boundary waters area near Ely, Minn. It is the only region in the lower 48 states (outside Alaska) where large numbers of wolves live. But just being there wasn't enough.

Sometimes Jim would drag a deer killed by a car into his yard. That might draw hungry wolves in close enough to photograph. Other times Jim would track a pack for days, following the wolves' paw prints, as they stalked their prey. He would even howl at the wolves and listen to their reply to see how close they were. The more time he spent stalking wolves, the better he got at it.

WINTER HUNTERS

While many animals, including squirrels and some bears, hibernate in winter, wolves don't. They stay awake, hunting. Their soft, snowshoe-like paws keep them from sinking in frozen snow. The graceful predator can attack big game like elk or moose clumsily trying to flee. Wolves might even attack a hibernating bear. Most wouldn't dare do that when the bear is awake.

PATIENCE AND GOOD LUCK

Jim must be patient to get photos. Sometimes he goes for weeks without shooting a picture. Other times he gets lucky. Once, a mother wolf let him <u>peek</u> inside her den, where pups were sleeping.[3]

Brandenburg wants his photographs to tell the real story of wolves. Then, people might not fear them so. And perhaps someday more of our country will be like Minnesota, where wild wolves roam free.

Think Aloud

[3] I wonder what it felt like to peek inside a wolf den.

Take Notes: Have students write down three facts they learned about wolves. Ask students to share how these facts change the way they think about wolves.

Student Think Aloud

Use Copying Master number 5 to prompt students to share an interesting fact or detail the author included in the article.

"I noticed the author . . ."

Cultural Perspectives

About 12,000 years ago, people in the Middle East realized wolves could lead them to food and warn them of danger. People learned to raise wolf pups and trained them not to fear humans. These wolves were the ancestors of the dogs we keep as pets today.

Think and Respond

1. The writer says many people fear wolves. List one fact about wolves that might surprise people. *Possible responses: Wolves are actually shy around people; wolves would rather run away than attack a human.* **Critical**

2. The writer uses facts and descriptive details to help the reader picture what the wolves are doing. Describe a place in the article where you could picture the wolves in your mind. *Possible response: I could picture the wolves walking across the snow. The writer says they have big paws like snowshoes.* **Genre**

3. At the end of the article, the author explains that Jim Brandenburg wants to teach people about wolves so they won't fear them. Do you think the author feels the same way? *Possible response: Yes, because she wrote this article and it gives us information about what wolves are really like.* **Author's Purpose**

The Sure-Footed Shoe Finder

from *Here's What You Do When You Can't Find Your Shoe*
by Andrea Perry

Genre: Poem

Poetic Element: Rhyme

Comprehension Strategy: Visualize

Think-Aloud Copying Master number 3

Before Reading

Genre: Tell students that you will read aloud a poem that contains a rhyming pattern. Remind students that rhyming words end with the same sound. Provide some examples such as *blue/shoe* and *dot/spot*. Explain that poets often use rhyme to add a musical quality to the poem.

Expand Vocabulary: Help students better understand the poem by introducing these words before reading:

> *mate:* one of a matching pair

> *lurch:* to move forward quickly and awkwardly

> *mere:* only

Set a Purpose for Reading: For the first reading, have students listen and enjoy how the rhyming pattern contributes to the humor of the selection.

During Reading

Emphasize the rhythm and rhyme of the poem as you read. Read through the poem without interruptions. Then reread, pausing to draw students' attention to the comprehension Think Alouds.

The Sure-Footed Shoe Finder

from *Here's What You Do When*
You Can't Find Your Shoe

by Andrea Perry

Genre Study

Poem: A couplet is
two successive lines of
verse that rhyme.

How many times has this happened to you?

You're late for the school bus and can't find a shoe.

It might take you two hours unless you have got

the Sure-Footed Shoe Finder there on the spot!

Just lift up the lever and open the gate

then toss in the shoe that is missing its <u>mate</u>.

With a beep and a clang and a stagger and <u>lurch</u>,

the Shoe Finder's off on its shoe-finding search.[1]

Think Aloud

[1]*I am able to picture in my mind this imaginary machine because the poet uses the words* beep *and* clang *here. These words describe sounds and help me imagine the type of machine it might be.*

The powerful Foot-Odor-Sensitive Vent

tracks down your sneaker by matching its scent,

and <u>mere</u> seconds later the shoe is retrieved.

You won't miss the school bus! Now aren't you

relieved?

Most of our customers happen to choose

our standard shoe model for footwear they lose,

although the new jumbo Shoe Finder can trace

even those snow boots you children misplace!

After Reading

Set a Purpose for Rereading: Once you have read aloud the poem for students' enjoyment, reread it for the purpose of having students identify rhyming words and the rhyming pattern. Ask students how the author's use of rhyme and humor add to their enjoyment of the poem.

Student Think Aloud

Use Copying Master number 3 to prompt students to share one detail the poet used to help them picture the shoe finder.

"I was able to picture in my mind . . . "

Think and Respond

1. Do you think an invention like this would be popular? Why or why not? *Possible response: Yes, because many people have trouble finding their shoes.* **Critical**

2. What do you notice about the rhyming words in the poem? *Possible responses: The rhyming words come at the end of the line; the last word of every two lines has the same sound.* **Poetic Element**

3. Why do you think the poet wrote this poem? *Possible responses: I think this poem is just for fun; I think she wanted to make people laugh at her imaginary invention.* **Author's Purpose**

Galileo and the Moons of Jupiter

by Tony Helies

Genre: Expository Nonfiction

Comprehension Strategy: Generate Questions

Think-Aloud Copying Master number 6

 Before Reading

Genre: Explain to students that you will read aloud a selection about Italian scientist Galileo and how he discovered the planet Jupiter's four moons. Remind students that they will learn about real people and real events because this is expository nonfiction.

Expand Vocabulary: Introduce the following words to students before reading:

> *orbited:* circled around
>
> *astronomer:* someone who studies the stars and planets
>
> *startling:* surprising
>
> *evidence:* proof

Set a Purpose for Reading: Have students listen to learn about the events that led to Galileo's discovery.

 **During Reading**

Use the comprehension Think Alouds during the first reading of the story. Notes about the genre and cultural perspectives may be used during subsequent readings.

Galileo and the Moons of Jupiter
by Tony Helies

Four hundred years ago, most people believed that Earth was the center of the universe. They thought that everything in the heavens, including the planets and the Sun, <u>orbited</u> our world.

An <u>astronomer</u> named Nicolaus Copernicus had written a book with a <u>startling</u> new theory: All planets, including Earth, orbit the Sun. Was Copernicus right or wrong?

In 1609, the Italian scientist and mathematician Galileo Galilei heard about a new device invented in Holland. Galileo thought it could help answer this question. The new instrument let the eye see distant objects as if they were nearby. It was the first telescope.

The early telescopes were made with two pieces of curved glass, called lenses, set into a metal tube. Telescope lenses are like the lenses in eyeglasses. Both types of lenses work on the same principle: Curved glass bends light. Telescope lenses are designed so this bending magnifies objects, making them look closer.[1]

Galileo was excited by the idea of using this new invention to look at the heavens. But these early telescopes were not powerful enough for astronomy. So Galileo set about building a better one. He worked for six months, experimenting with different designs. His hard work paid off. The telescope he built made objects look thirty times closer than they did with the eye alone.

On January 7, 1610, Galileo pointed his telescope toward one of the brightest objects in the night sky, the planet Jupiter. On either side of Jupiter, he saw little points of light arranged in a straight line, two to the left and one to the right.[2]

Galileo believed these were fixed stars, and expected they would remain in place as Jupiter moved across the sky.

The next night, he was surprised to find that the three stars were all to the right of Jupiter.

Galileo was puzzled. He had expected to find the stars farther to the left of Jupiter. What had caused them to move to the right? He waited impatiently to see where these stars would be on the third night, but cloudy skies blocked his view.

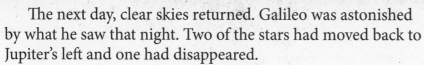

The next day, clear skies returned. Galileo was astonished by what he saw that night. Two of the stars had moved back to Jupiter's left and one had disappeared.

Galileo suspected that the third object was behind Jupiter.

Over the next two nights, the three stars continued to move from one side of Jupiter to the other. Galileo now realized that the three points of light he was observing were orbiting Jupiter. They were moons, not stars.

Galileo had proved that not all heavenly bodies orbit Earth. The Earth was not at the center of everything after all. This was the first evidence supporting Copernicus's theory. It helped create our modern view of the universe.[3]

On January 13, Galileo saw a fourth moon, which had been hidden behind Jupiter. These four moons—Io (EYE-oh), Europa (your-OH-pah), Ganymede (GAN-ih-meed), and Callisto (kuh-LIH-stoh)—are today known as the Galilean moons, in his honor.

Think Aloud

[3] I think this paragraph is important because it explains what Galileo's discovery meant. In Galileo's time, most people believed that all objects in space circled around Earth. Galileo proved that this was not true.

Summarize: Work with students to summarize the events that took place over five nights and led to Galileo's amazing discovery. Help students by reading aloud passages.

Student Think Aloud

Use Copying Master number 6 to prompt students to share a part of the selection they thought was important or helped them better understand the topic.

"I thought _____ was important because _____"

Cultural Perspective

Have students discuss what they have studied about astronomy or the solar system in science. The world's first telescopes were used to spot advancing armies or ships, not to study outer space. Today, nations from around the world use telescopes to look deep into space. Scientists from the United States, the United Kingdom, Chile, Australia, Argentina, and Brazil share two of the world's largest telescopes, the Gemini North, located in Hawaii, and its sister telescope, Gemini South, in Chile.

Think and Respond

1. The writer says Galileo spent six months building a telescope. Why does he say Galileo's "hard work paid off"? *Possible responses: Galileo's telescope was very powerful and helped him see stars far away; Galileo could see Jupiter with his new telescope and this led to his discovery about the orbits of the planets.* **Analytical**

2. List two facts that help us understand the sequence of events. *Possible responses: In 1609; On January 7, 1610* **Genre**

3. This article describes one of Galileo's important scientific discoveries. How does the writer help you understand the topic? *Possible response: The writer describes the important events in sequence order. It is easier to understand what Galileo did each night and what he learned.* **Author's Purpose**

Writers

by Jean Little

Genre: Poem

Poetic Elements: Rhythm and Rhyme

Comprehension Strategy: Make Inferences and Analyze

Think-Aloud Copying Master number 4

Before Reading

★ **Genre:** Tell students you will read aloud a poem about two friends. Explain that the first two lines of every stanza rhyme.

Expand Vocabulary: Introduce the following words before reading to help students understand the poem:

    poetic: relating to poetry; something you typically find in a poem

    crocuses: a flower that blooms in early spring

    aglow: glowing with light

    delight: to enjoy

Set a Purpose for Reading: For the first reading, have students listen and enjoy the language of the poem. Then ask students to listen for the rhyming words in the poem.

During Reading

Read through the poem the first time without interruptions. Then reread, pausing to draw students' attention to the comprehension Think Alouds. Emphasize how the first two lines of each stanza rhyme and how the last line sounds more like conversation.

Writers

by Jean Little

Emily writes of poetic things
Like crocuses and hummingbirds' wings,
But I think people beat hummingbirds every time.[1]

Emily likes to write of snow
And dawn and candlelight aglow.
But I'd rather write about me and Emily and stuff like that.

The funny thing is, I delight
To read what Emily likes to write,
And Emily says she thinks my poems are okay, too.

Also, sometimes, we switch with each other.
Emily writes of a fight with her mother.
I tell about walking alone by the river,
—how still and golden it was.

I know what Emily means, you see.
And, often, Emily's halfway me. . .
Oh, there's just no way to make anybody else understand.

We're not a bit the same and yet,
We're closer than most people get.
There's no one word for it. We just care about each other
the way we are supposed to.

So I can look through Emily's eyes
And she through mine. It's no surprise,
When you come right down to it, that we're friends.

Think Aloud

[1] *I figured out that beat does not mean "to hit or strike someone" in this line. Instead, the speaker is saying that for a poem people are better subjects for a poem than hummingbirds are.*

Genre Study

Poem: The first two lines of each stanza end with rhyming words. The poet writes a third line to each stanza that is much longer and does not rhyme. In this way the poet gives a different emphasis and rhythm to the third line of each stanza.

After Reading

Set a Purpose for Rereading: Reread the poem for the purpose of discussing friendship as it is described. Encourage students to write their own poems about friendship, friends, or what friendship means to them comparing the two friends and exploring the poem's deeper meanings. For example, discuss what it means when the two characters switch with each other, or how "Emily is halfway me."

Student Think Aloud

Use Copying Master number 4 to prompt students to discuss one place in the poem where they figured out the meaning of a word or phrase, or what the poet was trying to say.

"I figured out _____ because _____."

Think and Respond

1. The speaker says the two friends are "not a bit the same." Why do you think two people who are so different can be friends? *Possible responses: Even though they write about different things, they understand each other; friends don't have to like doing all the same things.* **Analytical**

2. Other than their rhymes, what do the pairs of rhyming lines have in common? *Possible response: The beat or rhythm of the lines is similar. They both like to read what the other one wrote.* **Genre**

3. What message do you think Jean Little wanted to share with her readers? *Responses may vary. Possible response: It is possible for two people to be very different and still be best friends.* **Author's Purpose**

Eating International

by Dee Murphy, R.D., L.D.

Genre: Realistic Fiction

Comprehension Strategy: Monitor Comprehension

Think-Aloud Copying Master number 2

Before Reading

Genre: Explain to students that the selection you will read aloud is a made-up story that could have happened in real life. Read the abbreviations after the author's name and explain that these show she is a dietician, or a specialist who studies nutrition. The author wraps what she knows about food into a story involving fictional characters.

Expand Vocabulary: To help students understand the variety of ethnic foods, introduce the following words before reading:

> *nibbled:* ate very little
>
> *patty:* a small flour cake of chopped food
>
> *soybeans:* edible seeds of a bushy plant
>
> *fondue:* a dip containing melted cheese

Set a Purpose for Reading: Invite students to listen to find out about foods that are popular in other countries.

During Reading

Use the comprehension Think Alouds during the first reading of the story. Notes about the genre and cultural perspective may be used during subsequent readings.

Eating International

by Dee Murphy, R.D., L.D.

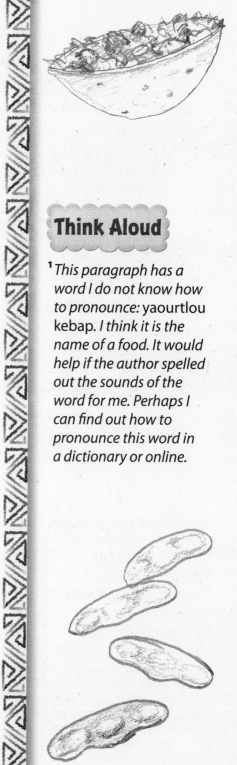

Nick Gianopolis <u>nibbled</u> at his cheeseburger and french fries.

"Don't you feel well today, Nick?" his friend Hiroshi asked. "You're not eating much."

Nick sighed and said, "I'm trying to think of something to write for the school newspaper. I have to turn in an article tomorrow, and I am fresh out of ideas. Plus, I wish they served food here like they do in my home country of Greece. I am so hungry for yaourtlou kebap right now."[1]

"Yaourtlou what?" asked Hiroshi.

Nick laughed. "It's a lamb burger with yogurt sauce served in pita bread. It's really good. You should try it."

"What's in it?" asked Hiroshi.

"It's a <u>patty</u> of ground lamb meat, egg, bread, onions, and spices. You grill it and put it in a pita pocket. Then you cover it with tomatoes, peppers, more onions, and top it off with yogurt sauce. Mmm! My mouth is watering just thinking about it."

Hiroshi thought for a minute. "I like edamame. In fact, maybe I'll have Mom make me some after school today. Do you want to come over?"

"I'm not sure," Nick said. "What is edamame?"

"Oh, it's wonderful!" said Hiroshi. "Edamame is 'sweet beans.' You boil fresh <u>soybeans</u> for a few minutes and eat them. They're very good."

Nick's eyes got wide. "You eat the shell and all?"

Hiroshi laughed. "No, no. You throw the shell away and just eat the beans. Soybeans grow in America. I'm not sure why many Americans have never heard of edamame. Japanese people eat it as a snack."

"I'll bet there are a lot of foods that people have never heard about," Nick said. He suddenly jumped up. "Hey, that would make a great article for the newspaper. I'll see you later, Hiroshi."

The Melting Pot

Nick researched several cookbooks from the library and talked to as many people as he could that afternoon. By evening he was tired, but he excitedly wrote his article.

Think Aloud

[1] *This paragraph has a word I do not know how to pronounce:* yaourtlou kebap. *I think it is the name of a food. It would help if the author spelled out the sounds of the word for me. Perhaps I can find out how to pronounce this word in a dictionary or online.*

America is a melting pot of cultures.[2] When people from these various cultures came to this country, they brought their recipes with them. But many people here have never tasted what the melting pot has to offer. Tasty, nutritious foods that are common in other countries haven't become popular here. But I will tell you about some of the mouthwatering dishes that you might be missing. Move over cheeseburgers and fries, and make way for some exciting ethnic foods!

Jan Van Beek says that his family makes kaasdoop every year at Christmas time.[3] Kaasdoop is a Gouda cheese fondue that is served with potatoes and rye bread. Jan's great-great-grandparents came from Holland and brought the recipe with them.

"Gouda cheese comes with a red wax wrapped around it. It's got a real mild, nutty flavor. I like to dip the bread in the melted cheese fondue," says Jan.

Emma Watertown's great-grandparents came to America from Germany. Rouladen is one of the German foods that Emma likes to make and enjoy.

"I get to help make rouladen when I visit my grandmother," says Emma. "First, we pound steaks until they are flat. Then we lay bacon, onion, cucumber slices, and spices on top of the flattened steak. Grandmother says you can put other meats or cheeses in it, but I like it this way. Finally, we roll it up and stick toothpicks in it to make sure it stays rolled. After it is cooked, we eat it with noodles, potato dumplings, and a salad."

Nadia Wolkoff says when she gets tired of drinking soda, she gets thirsty for kompot. Kompot is popular in the former Soviet Union, where many different kinds of fruit are grown.

"My mother keeps kompot on hand in the summer because it makes a good afternoon snack," says Nadia. "It's easy to make, and it's healthier than soda. You take any kind of fruit you want and boil it with sugar. When it's almost done cooking, you add cinnamon and nutmeg and stir. You can either drink it hot or cold. I like it hot in the winter and cold in the summer."

People who live in Denmark, Sweden, and Norway enjoy red cabbage. One recipe combines shredded red cabbage cooked in butter and sugar with a vinegar sauce for a sweet-and-sour delight. You can even add chopped apples for extra flavor. Yum!

After Reading

Take Notes: Have students list one of the foods they learned about in the article. Ask them to include a short description of the food and identify its country of origin.

Student Think Aloud

Use Copying Master number 2 to prompt students to share a connection they made between the text and their own life.

"I made a connection when . . ."

Cultural Perspective

Discuss how language in different neighborhoods or regions can vary depending upon the culture. (Examples might include *sandwiches*, *subs*, *heroes*, and *grinders*.)

Think and Respond

1. Why do you think Nick chose foods people eat as a topic for an article for his school newspaper? *Possible response: He thinks students would be interested to learn about foods from other countries and cultures.* **Critical**

2. How can you tell this is a story? *Possible responses: It has characters. There is dialogue. It tells a story about two boys at lunch, talking about what they like to eat.* **Genre**

3. Why do you think the author uses a fictional story to present factual information about foods from around the world? *Possible responses: Maybe she includes students in the story so readers can identify with them and their situation at lunchtime. Maybe she wanted to share information in a fun way.* **Author's Purpose**

A BIRTHDAY RIDDLE

by Lana Renetzky

Genre: Fiction

Comprehension Strategy: Analyze Story Structure

Think-Aloud Copying Master number 4

Before Reading

Genre: Tell students you will be reading a fiction selection aloud, and that fiction is a story with made-up characters and events. Remind students that the main character in a story often has a problem he or she must solve. The plot of the story tells how the character goes about solving the problem.

Expand Vocabulary: To help students follow the story's plot, introduce the following words before reading:

> *handy:* useful
>
> *chuckled:* laughed
>
> *reel:* the part of a fishing pole that the fishing line is wound around
>
> *billfold:* a man's wallet

Set a Purpose for Reading: Have students listen to the story to find out what Matthew's problem is and how he solves it.

During Reading

Use the comprehension Think Alouds during the first reading of the story. Notes about the genre and cultural perspective may be used during subsequent readings.

A BIRTHDAY RIDDLE

by Lana Renetzky

"What's handy for catching flies?'" Matthew laughed as he read the riddle tied to his birthday gift.[1] "It's a jelly sandwich? You got me a jelly sandwich for my birthday?"

Matthew's father chuckled. "No, Matthew. Guess again."

"One of Mom's pies," said Matthew.

"Try again," said his father.

"I think I know what it is," said Matthew. "Is it a baseball glove?"

"Right!"

Matthew tore the wrapping from the package. "All right!" he said, holding up the new glove. "It'll sure be handy for catching flies," he added with a grin.

Matthew's family always put riddles on the gifts they gave. The riddle was a hint about what was inside. But you could open the gift even if you couldn't guess the riddle.

Dad's birthday is coming soon, thought Matthew. *I want to find the perfect gift and make up the riddle myself.*

The next day Matthew's father was raking leaves. The rake looked rusty. *A new rake might be a good birthday gift*, thought Matthew. "Hi, Dad, how's the raking coming?" he asked.

"Fine," said his father. "This old rake never lets me down." Matthew frowned. Dad didn't need a rake.

Later that day Matthew saw his father washing the car. *I wonder if Dad would like a new car brush for his birthday*, thought Matthew.

"Look at that car shine," said Matthew's father proudly. "This car brush does a great job."

On Saturday Matthew saw his father in the garage cleaning his fishing reel. *That reel looks old*, thought Matthew. *A new reel would be a good birthday gift.*

"This was Grandpa's reel," said his father, as if he had read Matthew's mind. "Grandpa and I had many good fishing trips together. Someday it will be yours."[2]

That evening Matthew thought about what his father had said. *I know what to give Dad for his birthday*, thought Matthew. *And I know what to say in the riddle, too.*

Think Aloud

[1] *I already know that a riddle is a fun problem that people can guess the answer to solve. I wonder why he has a riddle on his birthday present. I'll read on to find out.*

Think Aloud

[2] *I can figure out Matthew's problem. He can't think of a birthday gift for his dad. Every time Matthew has an idea for a gift, he discovers that his dad is already happy with what he has.*

His father's birthday was the next Saturday. Matthew's mother baked a special cake and invited Matthew's aunts and uncles to the party. After the cake was served, his father answered the riddles and opened his gifts.

"This next gift is from Matthew. Let's see what the riddle says," said Matthew's father. "What is useful and comes in a small package? Hmmm. Could it be a watch?"

"Try again, Dad," said Matthew.

"A billfold?"

"Guess again," said Matthew.

Matthew's father thought hard.

Finally he said, "I'm stumped. OK if I open it now?"

Matthew nodded.

Matthew's father opened the box and read the note tucked inside.

"Dad—my gift is that I'll help you rake leaves and wash the car. And I'll be your partner when you go fishing. Love, Matthew."

"What a wonderful gift," said Matthew's father. "How about a fishing trip next weekend? You can use Grandpa's reel."

"All right!" said Matthew. He grinned. He had solved the riddle of finding the perfect gift for his dad.

After Reading

Retell the Story: Invite students to take turns retelling the events of the story.

Student Think Aloud

Use Copying Master number 4 to prompt students to share one thing they learned about Matthew or his dad based on the character's words or actions.

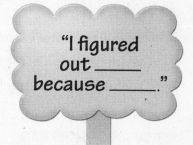

"I figured out _____ because _____."

Cultural Perspective

Many ancient books and stories include riddles. Riddles can be found in the Bible, the Koran, Greek myths, and Sanskrit manuscripts. Discuss stories from other cultures that include riddles.

Think and Respond

1. Do you think Matthew's dad will enjoy Matthew's gift more than a new rake or car brush? *Possible responses: Yes, Matthew's dad already had all the things he needed. Yes, Matthew's gift is to spend time with his dad and help him around the house.* **Critical**

2. How did Matthew solve his problem? *Possible responses: Matthew tried to find out what his dad needed. Matthew realized his dad didn't need a new rake or a brush, so he decided the best gift would be to help his dad.* **Genre**

3. What message do you think the author wants to share with readers? *Possible responses: Not all gifts have to be something you buy at a store. It feels good when you give someone a special gift.* **Author's Purpose**

WALK LIGHTLY

by J. Patrick Lewis

Genre: Poem

Poetic Element: Personification

Comprehension Strategy: Make Inferences and Analyze

Think-Aloud Copying Master number 6

Before Reading

Genre: Tell students you will read aloud a poem about the natural world. Explain that the names of places have been capitalized even though they are not proper nouns. This gives added emphasis to these places and is a way to personify them, or give them human qualities.

Expand Vocabulary: To help students better understand the poem's imagery, introduce these words before reading:

> *companion:* a friend
>
> *lightly:* softly
>
> *grandeur:* beauty
>
> *eternity:* forever

Set a Purpose for Reading: Have students listen for how the poet feels about the Earth.

During Reading

Read the poem expressively to convey the poet's love and personification of the natural world. Read through the poem the first time without interruptions. Then reread, pausing to draw students' attention to the comprehension Think Aloud.

WALK LIGHTLY

by J. Patrick Lewis

Make the Earth your <u>companion</u>.

   Walk <u>lightly</u> on it, as other creatures do.

Let the Sky paint her beauty—she is always
   watching over you.

Learn from the Sea how to face harsh forces.

Let the River remind you that everything will pass.

Let the Lake instruct you in stillness.

Let the Mountain teach you <u>grandeur</u>.

Make the Woodland your house of peace.

Make the Rainforest your house of hope.

Meet the Wetland on twilight ground.

Save some small piece of Grassland for a red kite
   on a windy day.

Watch the Icecaps glisten with crystal majesty.

Hear the Desert whisper hush to <u>eternity</u>.

Let the Town bring you togetherness.

Make the Earth your companion.

   Walk lightly on it, as other creatures do.[1]

Genre Study

Personification:
The poet personifies nature, or makes it seem like a real person. He uses the word *she* to give the impression that the sky is a woman. He gives the sky human actions such as painting with beautiful colors and watching over the earth.

Think Aloud

[1] *I thought the last two lines of the poem were important because this is also how the poem starts. I think the poet repeats these lines because he wants us to really think about and remember what he is saying.*

After Reading

Set a Purpose for Rereading: Reread the poem for the purpose of exploring the poet's message.

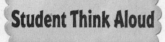

Use Copying Master number 6 to prompt students to discuss a line or an image they thought was important.

"I thought _____ was important because _____."

Think and Respond

1. What do you think the poet means when he says "walk lightly"? *Possible responses: Don't harm Earth; be gentle.* **Critical**

2. How does the poet personify, or give human characteristics to, the sky, mountain, and desert? Give some examples. *Possible responses: The poet describes them doing things that people do. The poet says the sky can paint, the mountain can teach, and the desert can whisper.* **Genre**

3. What do you think the poet is saying about the way people should treat Earth? *Possible responses: He is saying that we should be kind to Earth and treat it like a friend. The poet is saying we should take care of all the different places on Earth because they are beautiful.* **Author's Purpose**

From the Bellybutton of the Moon

Del ombligo de la luna

by Francisco X. Alarcón

Genre: Poem

Poetic Element: Imagery

Comprehension Strategy: Visualize

Think-Aloud Copying Master number 3

Before Reading

Genre: Tell students they will listen to a poem that was written in Spanish and translated into English. Explain that poems in any language include elements of a good description: words and phrases that appeal to the reader's senses and help him or her visualize what is being described.

Expand Vocabulary: To help students better understand the poem's imagery, introduce the following words before reading:

Atoyac: the name of a town in Mexico

familiar: describes something or someone you know well

gardenias: very fragrant flowers

origin: the place where your family is from

Set a Purpose for Reading: For the first reading, have students listen for how the poet feels about Mexico.

During Reading

If possible, have a native speaker read the stanzas in Spanish and then read the English translation. Read through the poem the first time without interruptions, using tone to emphasize the imagery. Then reread, pausing to draw students' attention to the genre note and the comprehension Think Aloud.

From the Bellybutton of the Moon
Del ombligo de la luna
by Francisco X. Alarcón

1. cuando / whenever
   digo / I say
   "México" / "Mexico"

   siento / I feel
   en la cara / the same wind
   el mismo viento / on my face

   que sentía / I felt when
   al abrir / I would open
   la ventanilla / the window

   en mi primer / on my first
   viaje al sur / trip south
   en coche / by car[1]

   veo / I see
   otra vez / Atoyac
   Atoyac / again

   el pueblo / the town
   donde se crió / where my mother
   mi madre / was raised

   y yo pasé / and I spent
   vacaciones / summer
   de verano / vacations

   oigo / I hear
   voces / familiar
   familiares / voices

   risas / laughter
   saludos / greetings
   despedidas / farewells

   huelo / I smell
   las gardenias / my grandma's
   de mi abuela / gardenias

Think Aloud

[1] I was able to picture in my mind the speaker riding in a car with the window down and the wind blowing in his face.

2. cuando
    digo
    "México"

    oigo
    a mi abuela
    hablándome

    de los Aztecas
    y de la ciudad
    que fundaron

    en una isla
    en medio
    de un lago

    "México"
    me dice
    mi abuela

    "significa:
    del ombligo
    de la luna"

    "no olvides
    tu origen
    mijo"

    quizás
    por eso
    mismo

    cuando
    ahora digo
    "México"

    quiero
    tocarme
    el ombligo

whenever
I say
"Mexico"

I hear
my grandma
telling me

about the Aztecs
and the city
they built

on an island
in the middle
of a lake

"Mexico"
says
my grandma

"means: from
the bellybutton
of the moon"

"don't forget
your origin
my son"

maybe
that's
why

whenever
I now say
"Mexico"

I feel
like touching
my bellybutton

After Reading

Set a Purpose for Rereading: Ask students if they have any questions before rereading the poem. Then reread the poem for the purpose of noting specific examples of imagery. Have students discuss examples of imagery that appealed to them the most.

Student Think Aloud

Use Copying Master number 3 to prompt students to tell about a place in the poem where they could visualize what the poet is describing.

"I was able to picture in my mind ..."

Cultural Perspective

Have students identify cultural aspects of the poem that they can relate to in their own lives. Francisco X. Alarcón began writing poetry when he was thirteen years old. He wanted to write down the words of the songs his grandmother sang to him. He thought his grandmother had been singing traditional Mexican folk songs, but he discovered that she had actually created the songs.

Think and Respond

1. Why do you think the poem is titled "From the Bellybutton of the Moon"? *Possible responses: The poet describes his memories of Mexico and his grandma said that Mexico means "from the bellybutton of the moon." The poet says when he thinks of Mexico he feels like touching his bellybutton.* **Analytical**

2. Identify a place in the poem where the poet used words or phrases that appealed to your senses. *Possible responses: the wind blowing on the boy's face (touch); hearing people talking and laughing (sound); smelling his grandma's flowers (smell)* **Poetic Element**

3. How do you think the poet feels when he thinks about Mexico? *Possible responses: He feels happy when he thinks of the summers he spent there. It makes him remember all the time he enjoyed spending with his grandma and listening to her stories.* **Author's Message**

Before You Came This Way

by Byrd Baylor

Genre: Poem

Poetic Element: Sensory Words/Imagery

Comprehension Strategy: Visualize

Think-Aloud Copying Master number 3

Before Reading

Genre: Tell students they will listen to a poem that includes descriptions of rock paintings created by people who lived long ago. Explain that seeing these paintings inspires the poet to think about the people who created them.

Expand Vocabulary: Introduce these words before reading to help students visualize the imagery of the poem:

wanderers: people who move from place to place

dim: hard to see

flick: move quickly, twitch

clink: a sharp sound

Set a Purpose for Reading: For the first reading, suggest that students enjoy listening to the language of the poem and that they try to visualize the paintings the poet describes.

During Reading

Read the poem slowly to convey the reflective, contemplative mood of the poet. Read through the poem the first time without interruptions. Then reread, pausing to draw students' attention to the genre note and the comprehension Think Aloud.

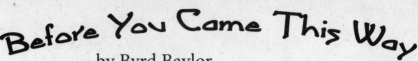

Before You Came This Way

by Byrd Baylor

You walk
down this canyon,
this place of
high red cliffs
and turning winds
and hawks that float
in a far white sky
and
you wonder:
"Am I the first one
ever
to come this way?"

And
you wonder:
"Is my footprint
the first one
ever
to touch this sand?"

But
then you see something
which tells you,
No,
you're not the first.
Your brothers
out of some
long ago lost age
passed this way, too.

You see their marks
on canyon walls.
Even the print
of their hands
is left,
chipped deep
in stone.

These men who came before you:
cliff dwellers,
hunters,
wanderers—
left messages
on rocks,
on cliff sides,
on steep rough
canyon walls.

They drew
the things
they did
and saw.
They even drew
their corn plants

and the birds
that flew above
their heads
and the paths
men cut
through nameless lands.

The reds
and yellows
and blacks
have been battered
by a thousand winds,
washed by a thousand rains.

The pictures are dim now,
half shadow,
but you search the canyon
for them.

And here
you see
young hunters
leap
in the morning sun.
The light still
gleams on their
arrows.

And here
a coyote
howls at the moon.

From his own hill
he guards his world.
He keeps the moon
in sight.

And rabbits flick
their ears
listening

listening

listening

while men do battle.
That fierce battle
raged
loud as thunder
across this canyon

Once

You find deer
with great antlers
branching like trees.

What is it they hear?

In the wind
there's the scent
of a mountain lion
who twitches his whiskers,
twitches his tail,
as he smiles
at himself. . .
or the deer.

Mountain goats
with curly horns.
Goats.
Goats.

More goats.
They drew them everywhere.
The <u>clink</u> of sharp hoofs
must have rung
as those goats jumped
from rock
to rock
to rock—

and then jumped back
where they had been
before . . . .[1]

High on a rock
someone drew
tracks of all the birds
he'd ever seen
and deer tracks,
lion tracks,
fox tracks . . .
even a wandering path
of the tracks of
men.

Men going where?
Searching for a
better place
for the tribe
to make its home?
Or for some newer
hunting ground?

Did pictures bring
strength
to the hunters?
Did they bring luck?
Was there some
magic
in the artist's hand?

There must have been magic
in songs and dances, too . . .

Think Aloud

[1] *I was able to picture in my mind the mountain goats coming alive on the walls of the canyon and jumping from rock to rock. The poet uses vivid descriptive words to share the way he sees the paintings.*

Songs to protect
hunters,
songs to make
children grow
and corn grow
and pumpkins.

People danced.
You ALMOST know
how it must have been.
Long lines of dancers
move
into the shadows.

You ALMOST hear
the chanting
and the flute
and the rattles
and the drums
that called down rain
and made the night winds
blow.

Sometimes
the dancers put on
masks.
Their artists drew
those great fierce faces
with headdresses
so tall and bright
and feathery
that they looked
part bird
part sky,
part mountain—
no longer men at all.

And
this canyon
echoed
with their voices.

Did they ever
wonder
who
in some far later time
would stand
in their
canyon
and think of them
and ALMOST hear
the echo of those voices
still in the wind?

Set a Purpose for Rereading: As you reread the poem, have students identify details and sensory words that refer to a different time and a different culture.

Student Think Aloud

Use Copying Master number 3 to prompt students to tell about one place in the poem where they can picture what the poet is describing.

"I was able to picture in my mind …"

Cultural Perspective

Discuss ancient art from other cultures. The oldest cave paintings were created 30,000 years ago in France. The ancient artists used animal fat, clay, and charcoal for paint. They used feathers, sticks, and their fingers as paintbrushes.

Think and Respond

1. How do the paintings help the poet imagine what life was like in the canyon long ago? *Possible responses: The paintings show the daily life of these people. The paintings show things the people saw, like birds, coyotes, and rabbits. He sees the pictures and imagines the people hunting and dancing.* **Analytical**

2. The speaker uses sensory words to describe the paintings. What words help the paintings come alive through sight, sound, smell, and touch? *Possible responses: leap, light still gleams, listening, scent, loud as thunder, clink, chanting, flute, rattles, bright, feathery, echoed* **Genre**

3. What do you think the poet wants his readers to learn from this poem? *Possible responses: I think he wants us to learn about the lives of the people who made the paintings. Perhaps he wants us to learn about things people did a long time ago. He wants us to see that we can learn about people through the art they created.* **Author's Purpose**

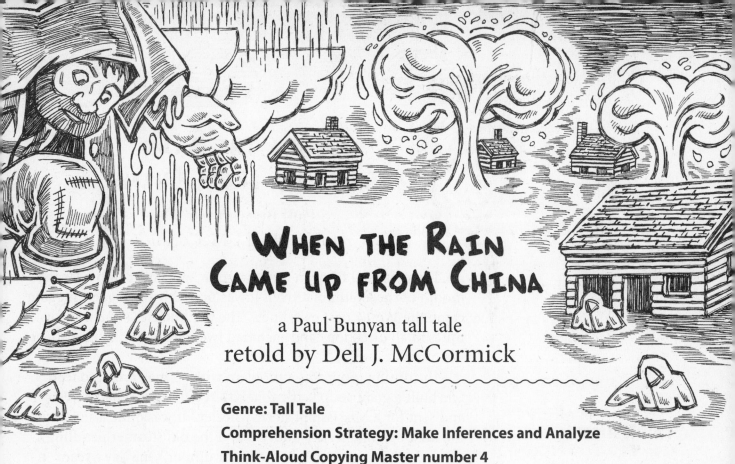

WHEN THE RAIN CAME UP FROM CHINA

a Paul Bunyan tall tale
retold by Dell J. McCormick

Genre: Tall Tale

Comprehension Strategy: Make Inferences and Analyze

Think-Aloud Copying Master number 4

 ## Before Reading

Genre: Explain that you will read aloud a tall tale about lumberjack Paul Bunyan. Tell students that a tall tale features a larger-than-life hero and story elements that are exaggerated to create humor. Explain that stories about Paul Bunyan began long ago in logging camps and were passed on through storytelling. The stories were popular with pioneers settling the American frontier.

Expand Vocabulary: Introduce these logging-related terms to students before reading:

>*stern-wheeler:* a steamboat that is driven by a paddle wheel
>
>*mackinaws:* heavy wool coats
>
>*cant hook:* a hooked tool used by a lumberjack
>
>*peavey:* a spiked tool used by a lumberjack

Set a Purpose for Reading: Invite students to listen for the exaggerations that the author uses to develop the story.

 ## During Reading

Use the comprehension Think Alouds during the first reading of the story. Notes about the genre and cultural perspective may be used during subsequent readings.

WHEN THE RAIN CAME UP FROM CHINA

a Paul Bunyan tall tale
retold by Dell J. McCormick

The year Paul Bunyan came west he had a big camp near the mouth of the Columbia River. It was probably the biggest logging camp the West Coast ever knew. The bunkhouses stretched for miles in all directions and each had five tiers of bunks, one above the other.

The dining room was a problem with so many men to feed. Ole built a giant soup kettle that covered five and a half acres and sent for a Mississippi stern-wheeler.[1] It was quite a sight with the fire burning merrily under it and the old steamer paddling around mixing up vegetable soup for dinner. One day a team of oxen fell in but it didn't worry Sourdough Sam any. He just changed the menu to "beef broth" that night and everybody seemed mighty pleased with the result.

The waiters wore roller skates, but the tables were so long they used to wear out two and three pair of skates just making the rounds with hot coffee. Tiny Tim the Chore Boy drove the salt and pepper wagon. He usually drove the length of the table and stayed all night at the far end, driving back to the kitchen in the morning for a fresh load. It took so much time getting all the men into the dining room some of them almost starved to death waiting their turn. Paul finally had to build lunch counters outside where the men waiting in line could get a light lunch in the meantime.

Paul expected a wet damp winter in the Douglas fir country, but month after month went by and never a sign of rain. He had all the bunkhouse roofs lined with thick tar paper to keep out the rain. The men were given rainproof slickers to put on over their mackinaws, and Babe the Blue Ox had a big tarpaulin for his own use. It was made from the canvas of Barnum and Bailey's main tent and fitted him fine except that it was a little short around the knees.

Just when they least expected it, however, it began to rain, and it was the strangest rain that anyone ever saw! Instead of raining down it rained up![2] The earth fairly spouted water. It filled the

Think Aloud

[1] *I know that in a tall tale everything is exaggerated or larger than it really could be. I see examples of exaggeration here. The writer says the pot for the soup covers five and a half acres and is so big a steamboat can fit inside of it.*

Think Aloud

[2] *This part is mostly about the strange rain. Why is the rain coming up out of the ground? How does this strange rain relate to China? As I continue to read, I think I will find out what the title means.*

men's boots. It rained up their sleeves. It went up their pant legs in spite of everything they could do. It was impossible to escape!

Naturally the rain coats and the tarpaulins and the tar roofs on the bunkhouses were useless, for the rain was coming up from below.

It seeped through the bunkhouse floors and flooded the cook shanty. Men crawled into the top bunks to escape and floated from one bunk to another on homemade rafts. Hot Biscuit Slim and Sourdough Sam cooked the evening meal floating around the kitchen on flour barrels. Cream Puff Fatty sat in an empty tub and paddled back and forth to the stove cooking apple pies.

Johnnie Inkslinger looked at the rain coming up from the ground and cried in great surprise:

"It's raining from China!"**3**

Up from China came the bubbling rain until the whole forest was one vast swamp. Little fountains of water sprang up everywhere. It rained in the men's faces when they bent over to pick up a cant hook or peavey. It spurted up their coatsleeves and ran down their backs inside their heavy mackinaws. A knothole in the bunkhouse floor started a geyser of water ten feet high. Paul decided to turn the bunkhouses upside down so the tar paper roofs would keep the water out. By that time the water was well up to his ankles, which meant that it would come up to the armpit of the average man.

Just as Paul had about decided to abandon the camp, the rain from China stopped as quickly as it began. The water seeped back into the moist earth, and by nightfall most of the water had disappeared except in pools here and there throughout the woods. Paul breathed a sigh of relief to find his feet on solid ground again, and the men built huge campfires to dry out their soaked clothing.

It was many years, however, before the lumberjacks in Paul's camp forgot their terrible experience with the rain that came from China. Even now when some camp orator starts to tell about a terrific rainstorm an old-timer will shake his head slowly and remark:

"Stranger, you don't even know what rain is unless you was with Paul Bunyan out in Oregon. You ain't never seen rain nor got wet unless you was working with Paul Bunyan out west the year the rain came up from China!"

Think Aloud

3 *I figured out what the title means because I see the men think there is so much rain in China that it has soaked all the way through to the other side of Earth!*

Genre Study

Tall Tale: While some tall tales may have a message, this story is meant to entertain listeners. The loggers and settlers who heard this story around the campfire would have enjoyed it purely for its humor.

Retell the Story: Invite students to draw the logging camp based on the story's larger-than-life descriptions. Have them use their drawings to retell the story.

Student Think Aloud

Use Copying Master number 4 to prompt students to discuss what they learned about the characters.

"I figured out ——— because . . ."

Cultural Perspective

The fictional character of Paul Bunyan may actually be based on a real person. Some experts say the first stories may have been told by Canadian loggers based on a real-life lumberjack named Joe Mufraw. Discuss with students the relevance of such entertainment in a pre-electronic culture.

Think and Respond

1. Why do you think people enjoy this type of story? *Possible responses: The stories are funny because they describe outrageous things that could not really happen. The lumberjacks could relate to the people in the stories and the things that happened to them.* **Critical**

2. Identify examples of exaggeration from the story. *Possible responses: The bunkhouses are several miles long. A ship can fit inside a soup pot. They have to carry salt and pepper in a wagon. The line for dinner is so long the men have to eat lunch while they are waiting.* **Genre**

3. Why do you think the author uses names like Hot Biscuit Slim, Sourdough Sam, Cream Puff Fatty, and Johnnie Inkslinger? *Possible responses: They add to the humor of the story. The names tell you something about each character.* **Author's Purpose**

Arachne the Spinner

a Greek myth
retold by Geraldine McCaughrean

Genre: Myth

Comprehension Strategy: Make Inferences and Analyze

Think-Aloud Copying Master number 4

Before Reading

Genre: Remind students that myths usually include gods or goddesses who have unique talents. Explain that the Greek goddess Athene was the goddess of the arts in ancient Greece. She was also considered a master weaver.

Expand Vocabulary: Help students use context clues to figure out the meaning of unfamiliar words. Introduce the following words before reading:

> *tapestries:* heavy woven cloths that were usually hung on walls
>
> *loom:* a machine for weaving yarn into fabric
>
> *shuttle:* a device used in looms to carry threads back and forth
>
> *irreverence:* not showing respect for someone or something

Set a Purpose for Reading: Have students listen to learn about Arachne's pride and downfall.

During Reading

First use the comprehension Think Alouds during the first reading of the story. Notes about the genre and cultural perspective may be used during subsequent readings.

Arachne the Spinner

a Greek myth
retold by Geraldine McCaughrean

Once, when all cloths and clothes were woven by hand, there was a weaver called Arachne more skillful than all the rest. Her tapestries were so lovely that people paid a fortune to buy them. Tailors and weavers came from miles around just to watch Arachne at work on her loom. Her shuttle flew to and fro, and her fingers plucked the strands as if she were making music rather than cloth.

"The gods certainly gave you an amazing talent," said her friends.

"Gods? Bodkins! There's nothing the gods could teach me about weaving. I can weave better than any god or goddess."

Her friends turned rather pale. "Better not let the goddess Athene hear you say that."

"Don't care who hears it. I'm the best there is," said Arachne.[1]

An old lady sitting behind her examined the yarns Arachne had spun that morning, feeling their delightful texture between finger and thumb. "So if there were a competition between you and the goddess Athene, you think you would win?" she said.

"She wouldn't stand a chance," said Arachne. "Not against me."

All of a sudden the old lady's gray hair began to float like smoke about her head and turn to golden light. A swish of wind blew her old coat into shreds and revealed a robe of dazzling white. She grew taller and taller until she stood head and shoulders above the crowd. There was no mistaking the beautiful gray-eyed goddess, Athene.

"Let it be so!" declared Athene. "A contest between you and me."

Arachne's friends fell on their faces in awe. But Arachne simply threaded another shuttle. And although her face was rather pale and her hands did tremble a little, she smiled and said, "A contest then. To see who is the best weaver in the world."

To and fro went the shuttles, faster than birds building a nest.

Athene wove a picture of Mount Olympus. All the gods were there: heroic, handsome, generous, clever, and kind. She wove all the creatures of creation on to her loom. And when

Think Aloud

[1] Arachne has a pretty bad attitude. She says things that are unkind and boastful. I think the author uses this language to exaggerate Arachne's pride.

she wove a kitten, the crowd sighed, "Aaaah!" When she wove a horse, they wanted to reach out and stroke it.

Alongside her sat Arachne, also weaving a picture of the gods.

But it was a comical picture. It showed all the silly things the gods had ever done: dressing up, squabbling, lazing about, and bragging. In fact she made them look just as foolish as ordinary folk.

But oh! when she pictured a butterfly sitting on a blade of grass, it looked as if it would fly away at any moment. When she wove a lion, the crowd shrieked and ran away in fright. Her sea shimmered and her corn waved, and her finished tapestry was more beautiful than nature itself.

Athene laid down her shuttle and came to look at Arachne's weaving. The crowd held its breath.

"You *are* the better weaver," said the goddess. "Your skill is matchless. Even I don't have your magic."

Arachne preened herself and grinned with smug satisfaction. "Didn't I tell you as much?"[2]

"But your pride is even greater than your skill," said Athene. "And your irreverence is past all forgiving." She pointed at Arachne's tapestry. "Make fun of the gods, would you? Well, for that I'll make such an example of you that no one will ever make the same mistake again!"

She took the shuttle out of Arachne's hands and pushed it into her mouth. Then, just as Athene had changed from an old woman into her true shape, she transformed Arachne.

Arachne's arms stuck to her sides, and left only her long, clever fingers straining and scrabbling. Her body shrank down to a black blob no bigger than an ink blot: an end of thread still curled out of its mouth.[3] Athene used the thread to hang Arachne up on a tree, and left her dangling there.

"Weave your tapestries forever!" said the goddess. "And however wonderful they are, people will only shudder at the sight of them and pull them to shreds."

It all came true. For Arachne had been turned into the first spider, doomed forever to spin webs in the corners of rooms, in bushes, in dark, unswept places. And though cobwebs are as lovely a piece of weaving as you'll ever see, just look how people hurry to sweep them away.

Think Aloud

[2]*At first I thought the goddess would win the contest. But now I find out that Arachne really is the best weaver in the world. I'm disappointed because I thought Arachne would learn a lesson about pride.*

Think Aloud

[3]*I can figure out that Athene turned Arachne into a spider because she shrank her body and turned her eight fingers into legs. I already know that spiders have eight legs. I also know that Arachne is a shortened form of the word* arachnid, *which means spider.*

After Reading

Retell the Story: Have students work in small groups to role play a scene from the story. Encourage them to create and use simple props in their retelling.

Student Think Aloud

Use Copying Master number 4 to prompt students to share why they think Athene changed Arachne into a spider.

"I figured out ____ because . . ."

Cultural Perspective

Discuss the universality of the Arachne story and point out that other cultures have stories about the theme of pride. See Anansi stories from West Africa.

Think and Respond

1. How do you think Arachne felt when Athene first appeared? How do you know this? *Possible responses: I think she felt scared but did not want to show her fear. The author says her hands were trembling and she was pale.* **Inferential**

2. Greek gods and goddesses have special character traits and powers. What do you learn about Athene from this story? *Possible responses: Athene is a skillful weaver and can change her shape. She can also change the shape of other people. She is wise and honest because she accepted defeat in the contest.* **Genre**

3. What can you learn from this myth about the dangers of too much pride? Give specific examples from the text. *Possible response: Too much pride can hurt you. Don't be too boastful because you might have to prove your words.* **Author's Purpose**

THE PEOPLE WHO HUGGED THE TREES

folk tale from India

adapted by Deborah Lee Rose

Genre: Folk Tale

Comprehension Strategy: Monitor Comprehension

Think-Aloud Copying Master number 8

Before Reading

Genre: Remind students that a folk tale often includes a moral or lesson about life. Ask students to discuss what kind of lesson they might learn from a folk tale about the environment.

Expand Vocabulary: Introduce the following words before reading:

precious: valuable

monsoon: a time of year when rainfall is very heavy

battering: striking or hitting in a violent way

fetched: brought back

Set a Purpose for Reading: Have students listen to find out what the title of the story means.

During Reading

Then use the comprehension Think Alouds during the first reading of the story. Notes about the genre and cultural perspective may be used during subsequent readings.

THE PEOPLE WHO HUGGED THE TREES

folk tale from India
adapted by Deborah Lee Rose

In long-ago India, when warrior princes ruled the land, there lived a girl who loved the trees. Her name was Amrita. Amrita lived in a poor village of mud houses, on the edge of the great desert. Just outside the village grew a forest. Every day Amrita ran to the forest, her long braid dancing behind her. When she found her favourite tree, she threw her arms around it. "Tree," she cried, "you are so tall and your leaves are so green! How could we live without you?" For Amrita knew that the trees shaded her from the hot desert sun. The trees guarded her from the howling desert sandstorms. And where the trees grew, there was precious water to drink.[1] Before she left the forest, Amrita kissed her special tree. Then she whispered, "Tree, if *you* are ever in trouble, I will protect you." The tree whispered back with a rustle of its leaves.

One day just before the monsoon rains, a giant sandstorm whirled in from the desert. In minutes the sky turned dark as night. Lightning cracked the sky and wind whipped the trees as Amrita dashed for her house. From inside, she could hear the sand battering against the shutters. After the storm ended, there was sand everywhere—in Amrita's clothes, in her hair and even in her food. But she was safe and so was her village, because the trees had stood guard against the worst of the storm.

As Amrita grew, so did her love for the trees. Soon she had her own children, and she took them to the forest with her. "These are your brothers and sisters," she told them. "They shade us from the hot desert sun. They guard us from the terrible desert sandstorms. They show us where to find water to drink," she explained. Then Amrita taught her children to hug the trees as she did.

Each day when she left the forest, Amrita fetched water from the village well. She carried the water in a large clay pot, balanced on top of her head. One morning by the well, Amrita spotted a troop of men armed with heavy axes. They were headed toward the forest. "Cut down every tree you can find," she heard the chief axeman say. "The Maharajah needs plenty of wood to build his new fortress."

The Maharajah was a powerful prince who ruled over many villages. His word was law. Amrita was afraid. "The tree-cutters

[1] I think this part is important because it shows why Amrita loves the trees so much. They provide shade and protection from sandstorms. The trees also show where to find water. These things are all very important to people who live in a desert.

will destroy our forest," she thought. "Then we will have no shade from the sun or protection from the sandstorms. We will have no way to find water in the desert!"[2] Amrita ran to the forest and hid. From her hiding place, she could hear the whack of the axes cutting into her beloved trees.

Suddenly Amrita saw the chief axeman swing his blade toward her special tree. "Do not cut down these trees!" she cried and jumped in front of her tree. "Stand back!" thundered the axeman. "Please, leave my tree," Amrita begged. "Chop me instead." She hugged the tree with all her strength. The axeman shoved her away and swung his blade. He could see only the tree he had been ordered to cut. Again and again the axeman chopped until Amrita's tree crashed to the ground. Amrita knelt down, her eyes filled with tears. Her arms tenderly grasped the tree's dying branches.

When news of Amrita's tree reached the village, men, women and children came running to the forest. One after another they jumped in front of the trees and hugged them. Wherever the tree-cutters tried to chop, the villagers stood in their way. "The Maharajah will hear of this!" threatened the chief axeman. But the people would not give in. The Maharajah was furious when the axemen returned emptyhanded. "Where is the wood I sent you to chop?" he stormed. "Your Highness, we tried to cut down the trees for your fortress," answered the chief axeman. "But wherever we went, the villagers hugged the trees to stop us." The Maharajah sliced the air with his battle sword. "These tree-huggers will pay for disobeying me!" He mounted his fastest horse and rode out for the forest. Behind him came many soldiers, riding long-legged camels and elephants with jeweled tusks.

The Maharajah found the people gathered by the village well. "Who has dared to defy my order?" he demanded. Amrita hesitated a moment, then she stepped forward "Oh Great Prince, we could not let the axemen destroy our forest," she said. "These trees shade us from the baking desert sun. They protect us from the sandstorms that would kill our crops and bury our village. They show us where to find precious water to drink."[3]

"Without these trees I cannot build a strong fortress!" the Maharajah insisted.

"Without these trees we cannot survive," Amrita replied. The Maharajah glared at her. "Cut them down!" he shouted.

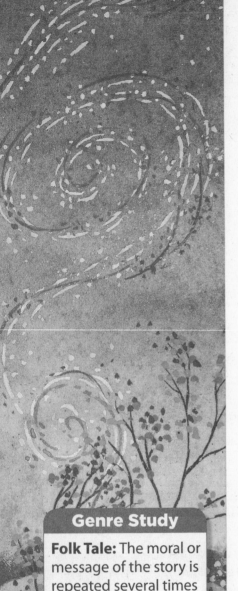

The villagers raced to the forest as the soldiers flashed their swords. Step by step the soldiers drew closer, as the sand swirled around their feet and the leaves shivered on the trees. Just when the soldiers reached the trees the wind roared in from the desert, driving the sand so hard they could barely see. The soldiers ran from the storm, shielding themselves behind the trees. Amrita clutched her special tree and the villagers hid their faces as thunder shook the forest. The storm was worse than any the people had ever known. Finally, when the wind was silent, they came slowly out of the forest.

Amrita brushed the sand from her clothes and looked around. Broken tree limbs were scattered everywhere. Grain from the crops in the field littered the ground. Around the village well drifts of sand were piled high, and Amrita saw that only the trees had stopped the desert from destroying the well and the rest of the village. Just beyond the well the Maharajah stood and stared at the forest. He thought for a long time, then he spoke to the villagers. "You have shown great courage and wisdom to protect your trees. From this day on your trees will not be cut," the Maharajah declared. "Your forest will always remain a green place in the desert."

The people rejoiced when they heard the Maharajah's words. They sang and danced long into the night and lit up the sky with fireworks. In the forest, the children strung flowers and bright colored paper through the branches of the trees. And where Amrita's tree had fallen, they marked a special place so they would never forget the tree's great sacrifice.

Many years have passed since that day, but some people say Amrita still comes to the forest to hug the trees. "Trees," she whispers, "you are so tall and your leaves are so green! How could we live without you?" For Amrita knows that the trees shade the people from the hot desert sun. The trees guard the people from the howling desert sandstorms. And where the trees grow there is water, and it is a good place for the people to live.

Genre Study

Folk Tale: The moral or message of the story is repeated several times rather than just at the end. This repetition is a way for the author to emphasize the importance of the message.

After Reading

Retell the Story: Have students pretend to be reporters telling the story of Amrita and how her village saved the forest from the Maharajah and his tree-cutters.

Student Think Aloud

Use Copying Master number 8 to prompt students to discuss a part of the story they thought was important.

"When I read _____ I had to read on . . ."

Cultural Perspective

Help students identify the characteristics of the setting (desert) and culture (agrarian India). Ask them to consider the universality of the theme across cultures and times. One modern-day attempt to save trees is called tree sitting. This is when someone builds a platform high up in a tree that is threatened and then the person lives day and night on the platform. The record for the world's highest "tree-sit" was reached when people sat in one of the world's tallest trees in the Styx forest in Tasmania.

Think and Respond

1. How do you know the Maharajah does not understand the true value of the forest? *Possible response: He thinks the forest is just trees. He does not know that the trees protect the village from the sun and sandstorms. He just wants to use the trees to build a fortress.* **Analytical**

2. What does this folk tale teach about the environment? *Possible responses: It shows the importance of protecting natural resources. It shows that the people knew their needs better than their ruler did.* **Genre**

3. Why do you think this story still has an important message for today's readers? *Possible response: There are still places on Earth where forests are being destroyed. People need to think about the consequences of destroying our forests.* **Author's Purpose**

The Song of the World's Last Whale

by Pete Seeger

Genre: Folk Song

Poetic Element: Rhyme

Comprehension Strategy: Evaluate

Think-Aloud Copying Master number 2

Before Reading

Genre: Explain to students that you will read aloud the lyrics to a folk song. Remind them that lyrics are meant to be sung to music. The songwriter's goal in this song is to draw attention to an environmental crisis. The songwriter hopes people who hear the song will be moved to take action.

Expand Vocabulary: Introduce the following words before reading to help students understand the song:

> *reefed:* folded up to be made smaller
>
> *passionate:* with great love and emotion
>
> *harpoons:* spears used to hunt whales
>
> *fate:* the future

Set a Purpose for Reading: Invite students to listen for rhyming words as you read the lyrics aloud.

During Reading

Emphasize the serious tone of the song and its message concerning the crisis the last whale is facing. Read through the song the first time without interruptions. Then reread, pausing to draw students' attention to the comprehension Think Aloud and genre note.

The Song of the World's Last Whale

by Pete Seeger

I heard the song of the world's last whale,
As I rocked in the moonlight and reefed the sail.
It'll happen to you also without fail,
If it happens to me, sang the world's last whale.

It was down off Bermuda
Early last spring.
Near an underwater mountain
Where the humpbacks sing.
I lowered the microphone
A quarter mile down,
Switched on the recorder
And let the tape spin round.

I didn't just hear grunting,
I didn't just hear squeaks,
I didn't just hear bellows,
I didn't just hear shrieks.
It was the musical singing
And the passionate wail,
That came from the heart
Of the world's last whale.

Down in the Antarctic
The harpoons wait.
But it's upon the land
They decide my fate.
In London Town
They'll be telling the tale,
If it's life or death
For the world's last whale.

So here's a little test
To see how you feel,
Here's a little test
for this age of the automobile.
If we can save
Our singers in the sea,
Perhaps there's a chance
To save you and me.[1]

Think Aloud

[1] *I made a connection when the song offers a warning about the last whale and about saving humans.*

After Reading

Set a Purpose for Rereading: Reread the song for the purpose of exploring its deeper meanings, including the songwriter's message. Have students discuss the techniques or literary devices that the writer uses to influence the reader's attitudes and emotions. Encourage students to compare their responses to the song with the opinions and responses of their classmates.

Student Think Aloud

Use Copying Master number 2 to prompt students to share a connection they made while listening to the song.

"I made a connection when...."

Cultural Perspective

Discuss the significance of folk songs in different cultures. If possible have students listen to this folk song as well as others.

Think and Respond

1. What can you tell about the whale based on the kinds of sounds it makes? *Possible responses: You can tell the whale is upset because it is shrieking and making other unpleasant sounds. You can tell the whale feels strongly about something because it is crying from its heart.* **Analytical**

2. Some folk songs are meant to draw attention to an environmental crisis. What is the message of this song? *Possible responses: People need to protect the whales or someday they will all be gone. Humans and animals share the same world. What happens to animals could also happen to people.* **Genre**

3. What do you think Pete Seeger wants people to think and feel when they listen to his song? *Possible responses: He wants people to be upset about what is happening to the whales. He wants to persuade people to learn about what is happening to whales and do something to protect them.* **Author's Purpose**

Under the Back Porch
by Virginia Hamilton

Genre: Poem

Poetic Element: Sensory Words

Comprehension Strategy: Monitor Comprehension

Think-Aloud Copying Master number 2

Before Reading

Genre: Tell students they will listen to a poem in which the speaker describes spending time alone under the back porch. Ask students to imagine what this kind of place might be like. Have them describe what they might see, hear, smell, and touch in such a place.

Expand Vocabulary: Introduce the following words before reading:

> *damp:* wet
>
> *slants:* comes through at an angle
>
> *slats:* thin, flat strips of wood
>
> *moist:* a little bit wet

Set a Purpose for Reading: For the first reading, have students listen for words and details that appeal to the senses.

During Reading

Read softly to help convey the quiet and peacefulness the poet associates with her special place under the porch. Read through the poem the first time without interruptions. Then reread, pausing to draw students' attention to the comprehension Think Aloud and genre note.

Under the Back Porch

by Virginia Hamilton

Our house is two stories high
shaped like a white box.
There is a yard stretched around it
and in back
a wooden porch.

Under the back porch is my place.
I rest there.
I go there when I have to be alone.
It is always shaded and <u>damp</u>.
Sunlight only <u>slants</u> through the <u>slats</u>
in long strips of light,
and the smell of the damp
is <u>moist</u> green,
like the moss that grows here.

My sisters and brothers
can stand on the back porch
and never know
I am here
underneath.
It is my place.[1]
All mine.

Genre Study

Poem: The poet uses sensory words to help the reader experience what it is like to spend time in her place under the porch. These descriptive details also help the reader comprehend how the poet feels about this place.

Think Aloud

[1] *I can make a connection when the poet says the space under the back porch is her place. I can picture what it looks like. I have a special place at home where I like to spend time by myself, too.*

Set a Purpose for Rereading: Read the poem aloud again to students. Then have students use their senses to describe and write about a place that is special to them.

Student Think Aloud

Use Copying Master number 2 to prompt students to share a personal connection they made with the poem.

"I made a connection when . . ."

Think and Respond

1. Why do you think the speaker wants to be alone under the back porch? *Possible responses: She wants to have her own place. She wants to be away from her brothers and sisters.* **Analytical**

2. What descriptive details does the poet use to help the reader imagine what it feels like to be under the porch? *Possible responses: She says it is cool and shady, only pieces of light come through the boards, moss grows there, and it smells musty.* **Genre**

3. What can you tell about how the author feels about the place using information from the text? *Possible responses: It is a place she goes to be alone. She can go there and no one else knows where she is. She says the place is "all mine," so it is somewhere only she goes.* **Author's Purpose**

Music, Music for Everyone

by Vera B. Williams

Genre: Realistic Fiction

Comprehension Strategy: Summarize

Think-Aloud Copying Master number 7

Before Reading

Genre: Tell students you will read aloud a fiction selection. Remind students that this type of story often tells about a main character with a problem that needs to be solved. The plot of the story shows how the character deals with and solves the problem.

Expand Vocabulary: Introduce the following words before reading:

accordion: a portable keyboard with a hand-operated bellows that pushes wind past the reeds to create music

fiddle: a violin

company: guests

anniversary: a yearly date that marks a special occasion

Set a Purpose for Reading: Invite students to listen to identify the main character's traits, feelings, and motivations. Have them determine how these help her find a solution to her problem.

During Reading

Use the comprehension Think Alouds during the first reading of the story. Notes about the genre and cultural perspective may be used during subsequent readings.

Music, Music for Everyone

by Vera B. Williams

Our big chair often sits in our living room empty now. When I first got my <u>accordion</u>, Grandma and Mama used to sit in that chair together to listen to me practice. And every day after school while Mama was at her job at the diner, Grandma would be sitting in the chair by the window. Even if it was snowing big flakes down on her hair, she would lean way out to call, "Hurry up, Pussycat. I've got something nice for you."

But now Grandma is sick. She has to stay upstairs in the big bed in Aunt Ida and Uncle Sandy's extra room. Mama and Aunt Ida and Uncle Sandy and I take turns taking care of her. When I come home from school, I run right upstairs to ask Grandma if she wants anything. I carry up the soup Mama has left for her. I water her plants and report if the Christmas cactus has any flowers yet. Then I sit on her bed and tell her about everything.[1]

Grandma likes it when my friends Leora, Jenny, and Mae come home with me because we play music for her. Leora plays the drums. Mae plays the flute. Jenny plays <u>fiddle</u> and I play my accordion. One time we played a dance for Grandma that we learned in the music club at school.

Grandma clapped until it made her too tired. She told us it was like the music in the village where she lived when she was a girl. It made her want to dance right down the street. We had to keep her from trying to hop out of bed to go to the kitchen to fix us a treat.

Leora and Jenny and Mae and I left Grandma to rest and went down to get our own treat. We squeezed together into our big chair to eat it.

"It feels sad down here without your grandma," Leora said. "Even your big money jar up there looks sad and empty."[2]

"Remember how it was full to the top and I couldn't even lift it when we bought the chair for my mother?" I said.

"And remember how it was more than half full when you got your accordion?" Jenny said.

"I bet it's empty now because your mother has to spend all her money to take care of your grandma till she gets

Think Aloud

[1] I can tell the main character is a kind person. She helps take care of her grandma, takes her food, and spends time with her.

Think Aloud

[2] I think the main character's family is having a hard time because only the mom works and they don't have a lot of money. The grandmother is sick in bed now and the main character is worried. Music seems to bring the only happiness to this house.

better. That's how it was when my father had his accident and couldn't go to work for a long time," Mae said.

Mae had a dime in her pocket and she dropped it into the jar. "That will make it look a little fuller anyway," she said as she went home.

But after Jenny and Leora and Mae went home, our jar looked even emptier to me. I wondered how we would ever be able to fill it up again while Grandma was sick. I wondered when Grandma would be able to come downstairs again. Even our beautiful chair with roses all over it seemed empty with just me in the corner of it. The whole house seemed so empty and so quiet.

I got out my accordion and I started to play. The notes sounded beautiful in the empty room. One song that is an old tune sounded so pretty I played it over and over. I remembered what my mother had told me about my other grandma and how she used to play the accordion. Even when she was a girl not much bigger than I, she would get up and play at a party or a wedding so the company could dance and sing. Then people would stamp their feet and yell, "More, more!" When they went home, they would leave money on the table for her.

That's how I got my idea for how I could help fill up the jar again. I ran right upstairs. "Grandma," I whispered. "Grandma?"

"Is that you, Pussycat?" she answered in a sleepy voice. "I was just having such a nice dream about you. Then I woke up and heard you playing that beautiful old song. Come. Sit here and brush my hair."

I brushed Grandma's hair and told her my whole idea. She thought it was a great idea. "But tell the truth, Grandma," I begged her. "Do you think kids could really do that?"

"I think you and Jenny and Leora and Mae could do it. No question. No question at all," she answered. "Only don't wait a minute to talk to them about it. Go call and ask them now."

And that was how the Oak Street Band got started.

Our music teachers helped us pick out pieces we could all play together. Aunt Ida, who plays guitar, helped us practice. We practiced on our back porch. One day our neighbor

leaned out his window in his pajamas and yelled, "Listen, kids, you sound great but give me a break. I work at night. I've got to get some sleep in the daytime." After that we practiced inside. Grandma said it was helping her get better faster than anything.

At last my accordion teacher said we sounded very good. Uncle Sandy said so too. Aunt Ida and Grandma said we were terrific. Mama said she thought anyone would be glad to have us play for them.

It was Leora's mother who gave us our first job. She asked us to come and play at a party for Leora's great-grandmother and great-grandfather. It was going to be a special <u>anniversary</u> for them. It was fifty years ago on that day they first opened their market on our corner. Now Leora's mother takes care of the market. She always plays the radio loud while she works. But for the party she said there just had to be live music.

All of Leora's aunts and uncles and cousins came to the party. Lots of people from our block came too. Mama and Aunt Ida and Uncle Sandy walked down from our house very slowly with Grandma. It was Grandma's first big day out.

There was a long table in the backyard made from little tables all pushed together. It was covered with so many big dishes of food you could hardly see the tablecloth. But I was too excited to eat anything.

Leora and Jenny and Mae and I waited over by the rosebush. Each of us had her instrument all ready. But everyone else went on eating and talking and eating some more. We didn't see how they would ever get around to listening to us. And we didn't see how we could be brave enough to begin.

At last Leora's mother pulled us right up in front of everybody. She banged on a pitcher with a spoon to get attention.

Then she introduced each one of us. "And *now* we're going to have music," she said. "Music and dancing for everyone."

It was quiet as school assembly. Every single person there was looking right at Leora and Jenny and Mae and me. But we just stood there and stared right back.[3]

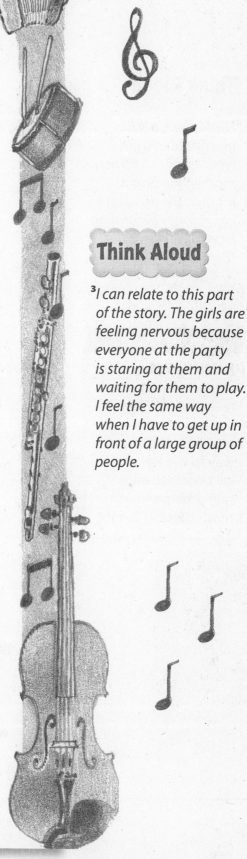

Think Aloud

[3] I can relate to this part of the story. The girls are feeling nervous because everyone at the party is staring at them and waiting for them to play. I feel the same way when I have to get up in front of a large group of people.

Think Aloud

4I think this story is mostly about a girl who wants to help her mother and Grandmother. She decides to earn money by forming a band with her three friends.

Genre Study

Realistic Fiction: The story ends with a realistic resolution of the main character's problem. She found a way to use her musical talents to entertain others and earn money for her family.

Then I heard my grandma whisper, "Play Pussycat. Play. Just like you used to play for me."

I put my fingers on the keys and buttons of my accordion. Jenny tucked her fiddle under her chin. Mae put her flute to her mouth. Leora held up her drums. After that we played and played. We made mistakes, but we played like a real band. The little lanterns came on. Everyone danced.

Mama and Aunt Ida and Uncle Sandy smiled at us every time they danced by. Grandma kept time nodding her head and tapping with the cane she uses now. Leora and Jenny and Mae and I forgot about being scared. We loved the sound of the Oak Street Band.**4**

And afterward everybody clapped and shouted. Leora's great-grandfather and great-grandmother thanked us. They said we had made their party something they would always remember. Leora's father piled up plates of food for us. My mama arranged for Leora, Jenny, and Mae to stay over at our house. And when we finally all went out the gate together, late at night, Leora's mother tucked an envelope with our money into Leora's pocket.

As soon as we got home, we piled into my bed to divide the money. We made four equal shares. Leora said she was going to save up for a bigger drum. Mae wasn't sure what she would do with her share. Jenny fell asleep before she could tell us. But I couldn't even lie down until I climbed up and put mine right into our big jar on the shelf near our chair.

Retell the Story: Have students create a character cluster map using words and phrases that describe the main character's traits, feelings, and motivations. Ask them to use the map to retell the story, identifying the setting and the problem and solution.

Student Think Aloud

Use Copying Master number 7 to prompt students to think about and discuss the story.

> "This was mostly about..."

Cultural Perspective

In this story, the narrator uses her gift of music to help her family and bring happiness to others. We do not know how far back music exists in the cultures of the world. People had music long before they had writing. Ask students to share what they know about music in their cultures.

Think and Respond

1. How has Grandma's illness affected the family? *Possible responses: The living room feels sad and empty because she is not there. The family has used up a lot of its savings to take care of her.* **Analytical**

2. How does the solution to the main character's problem fit the genre of realistic fiction? *Possible responses: She forms a band with her friends and earns money to help her family. All four girls already knew how to play musical instruments. They just had to practice. This could have happened in real life, so Music Music for Everyone is realistic fiction.* **Genre**

3. What was the author's purpose in writing this story? *The author wrote this to entertain and to remind readers that, when times are hard, solutions can be found by working together and using the talents that we have.* **Author's Purpose**

FROG AND LOCUST

a Pueblo folk tale
retold by Joe Hayes

Genre: Folk Tale

Comprehension Strategy: Make Inferences and Analyze

Think-Aloud Copying Master number 6

Before Reading

Genre: Tell students they will listen to a Pueblo Indian folk tale. Remind students that a folk tale is a story based on the traditions of a people or region. This folk tale explains the meaning behind a ritual, or ceremony, that is very important to the Pueblo people.

Expand Vocabulary: Introduce the following words and phrases to help students understand the folk tale:

> *locust:* a type of grasshopper
>
> *clung:* held on tightly
>
> *gathered:* collected
>
> *with one voice:* singing the same song together

Set a Purpose for Reading: Invite students to listen to find out what problem the frog and the locust share and what lesson they teach.

During Reading

Use the comprehension Think Alouds during the first reading of the story. Notes about the genre and cultural perspective may be used during subsequent readings.

FROG AND LOCUST

a Pueblo folk tale
retold by Joe Hayes

Once it didn't rain for a whole year. The grass turned brown and died. Trees and bushes lost their leaves. In the canyon bottom, where a lively stream usually flowed, there were just a few puddles of water left. And every day those puddles got smaller and smaller.

Living at the edge of one puddle was a frog. The frog saw his puddle get smaller with each passing day, and he knew that if it didn't rain the puddle would soon dry up. And he would die!

But the frog knew how to sing a rain song. So he sang to see if he could bring some rain. The frog croaked—

R-R-RAIN, R-R-RAIN, R-R-RAIN . . .

But his song wasn't loud enough to reach the top of the mountain, and that is where the Rain God lived. The Rain God couldn't hear the frog singing, and no rain came.[1]

Not far from the frog's puddle was a bush, and living in the bush was a locust. The locust knew that if it didn't rain, he wouldn't live through the summer. So as he clung to the bush the locust buzzed—

R-r-r-rain-n-n-n, r-r-r-rain-n-n-n . . .

But that song wasn't loud enough to reach the top of the mountain either. And when the locust saw that there were no clouds in the sky, and it wasn't going to rain, he started to cry—

Ee-he-he-he-he . . .[2]

The frog heard someone crying, so he hopped over there. He looked up and croaked—

WHAT'S THE MATTER-R-R. . .?
WHAT'S THE MATTER-R-R. . .?

The locust told him, "If it doesn't rain, I'm going to die!"
When the frog heard that, he thought about how the same thing would happen to him if it didn't rain, and he started to cry too—

WAH-WAH-WAH . . .

Think Aloud

[1]*The frog knows how to bring rain, but he can't sing loud enough by himself. I wonder how he will solve his problem. When I can't do something by myself, I ask someone to help me. Maybe the frog will ask the other frogs to sing with him.*

Think Aloud

[2]*I notice that the author uses the sounds of the frog and the locust to help tell the story. Frogs and locusts do not really say "R-R-RAIN" but it helps me picture the action in the story.*

Think Aloud

[3]*I thought this part was important because the author has shown me that the frog and the locust cannot sing loud enough alone, but now they are going to work together. Maybe the lesson of the story is that we can accomplish more by working together than by ourselves.*

Genre Study

Folk Tale: This story explains the origin of the Pueblo Indians' rain dance. This kind of story is used to help people understand the meaning behind one of the tribe's rituals and history.

But then the locust got an idea. He thought—when one person works all alone, he doesn't get much done. But when people work together, they can do a lot of work. So the locust said, "Frog, maybe we should sing together." The frog thought that was a good idea. So they added their songs together—

> R-R-RAIN . . . r-r-r-rain-n-n . . .
> R-R-RAIN . . . r-r-r-rain-n-n . . .

It still wasn't loud enough to go to the top of the mountain. But it was loud enough to go to the next puddle up the canyon. And living over there was another frog. On the other side of the canyon, there were even more frogs. They heard the frog sing and thought they would join in and sing along with him. They all sang—[3]

> R-R-RAIN, R-R-RAIN, R-R-RAIN . . .

In nearby bushes, and in the bunches of grass still growing at the puddle's edge, there were also more locusts. They heard the song and thought they'd join in too—

> R-r-r-rain-n-n, r-r-rain-n-n . . .

Soon all the frogs and locusts were singing—

> R-R-RAIN . . . r-r-rain-n-n . . .
> R-R-RAIN . . . r-r-rain-n-n . . .

It was a loud song! It went clear to the top of the mountain! The Rain God heard the song. He climbed up to the center of the sky and gathered dark clouds all around him. From the distant mountains he made the cool wind begin to blow. Rain drops started falling. The rain fell faster . . . and faster. It was a big storm!

The canyon stream filled back up with water. The trees and bushes got new leaves. The whole land came to life again. And it was all because the frogs and locusts worked together!

And that's why it is to this day that if one person's fields are dry and dying, he doesn't go off by himself and sing for rain. But all the people gather together. They dance with one heart, and with one voice they sing. And in that way they can always bring the rain.

After Reading

Retell the Story: Have students retell the story with a partner. Encourage them to pass the folk tale back and forth, including story details as well as the beginning, middle, and end. Each student tells a small part and then lets the other paraphrase what was said before recalling what happened next.

Student Think Aloud

Use Copying Master number 6 to prompt students to discuss a detail of the story they thought was important.

"I thought _____ was important because _____."

Cultural Perspective

The Pueblo are Native Americans who live in northwestern New Mexico and northeastern Arizona. Because they live in such a dry climate, rain has always been important to their culture. A common literary element of folk tales is to use wise talking animals as main characters. Have students share the names of other folk tales they have read that have wise animals in them.

Think and Respond

1. How are the frog and the locust alike? *Possible responses: They both know how to sing a rain song. They both need water to live.* **Analytical**

2. Folk tales often teach lessons about the culture which they are from. What does this folk tale teach about the culture of the Pueblo Indians? *Possible responses: The Pueblo work together as a group. They still sing and dance together as a way to bring needed rain.* **Genre**

3. What message do you think the author wants to share with readers? *Possible response: When people work together, they can accomplish more than if they worked alone.* **Author's Purpose**

The Runner
by Faustin Charles

Genre: Poem

Poetic Element: Figurative Language

Comprehension Strategy: Make Inferences and Analyze

Think-Aloud Copying Master number 4

Before Reading

Genre: Tell students they will listen to a poem that includes figurative language. Review the characteristics of a simile and a metaphor and give examples of each as needed. Explain that poets use figurative language to develop meaning or to highlight specific qualities. In this poem, the poet uses metaphor to compare a runner to several nonliving things that move with great speed.

Expand Vocabulary: Introduce the following words before reading:

> *swifter:* faster
>
> *outrunning:* running faster than
>
> *comet:* a collection of ice and dust that travels through space, appearing as a streak in the sky

Set a Purpose for Reading: For the first reading, have students listen and enjoy the language. With each comparison, invite students to picture the object of comparison in their minds.

During Reading

Read with expression to help students understand the sense of speed in the poem. Read through the poem the first time without interruptions. Then reread, pausing to draw students' attention to the comprehension Think Aloud and genre note.

The Runner

by Faustin Charles

Run, run, runner man,

As fast as you can,

Faster than the speed of light,

Smoother than a bird in flight.

Run, run, runner man,

No one can catch the runner man,

<u>Swifter</u> than an arrow,

<u>Outrunning</u> his own shadow.

Run, run, runner man,

Faster than tomorrow.

Run, run, runner man,

Quicker than a rocket!

Into deep space spinning a <u>comet</u>![1]

Run, run, runner man,

Lighting the heavens of the night,

Run, run, runner man,

Out of sight,

Run, run, runner man, run!

Genre Study

Poem: The poet repeats the line "Run, run, runner man" throughout the poem. This repetition creates a sense of the runner's non-stop speed and mimics the sound of his shoes repeatedly hitting the ground.

Think Aloud

[1] *I figured out that the poet compares the runner to a rocket and a comet because both of these are things that move very fast. The poet uses these comparisons to show me that the runner is also very fast.*

Set a Purpose for Rereading: Once you have read the poem aloud for students' enjoyment, reread it for the purpose of identifying rhyming words and rhythm.

Student Think Aloud

Use Copying Master number 4 to prompt students to share something they noticed about the poet's choice of words or images.

"I figured out ___ because . . ."

Think and Respond

1. How does the poet give the reader a sense of how fast the runner is? *Possible responses: He uses adjectives like* faster, swifter, *and* quicker. *He says the runner is faster than the speed of light and quicker than a rocket. The runner is so fast that he can outrun his shadow.* **Analytical**

2. To what things does the poet compare the runner? *Possible responses: the speed of light; a bird; an arrow; his shadow; a rocket; a comet* **Genre**

3. How do you think the poet feels about the runner? How can you tell?
Possible responses: The poet admires the speed of the runner. I can tell this because he describes the runner's abilities to make him seem superhuman. **Author's Purpose**

THE NAME OF THE TREE

a Bantu folk tale
retold by Celia Barker Lottridge

Genre: Folk Tale

Comprehension Strategy: Make Inferences and Analyze

Think-Aloud Copying Master number 2

Before Reading

Genre: Tell students they will listen to a folk tale from Africa. Have students recall another folk tale they have heard, "Frog and Locust." Tell students that this story also features a problem that the characters are trying to solve. Discuss how the animals solved their problem in "Frog and Locust."

Expand Vocabulary: Introduce the following words before reading:

plain: an area of land that is flat and has no trees

pomegranates: red fruits that are the size of oranges

strode: walked with long steps

haughtily: in a very proud way

Set a Purpose for Reading: Invite students to listen to find out what problem the animals are having.

During Reading

Use the comprehension Think Alouds during the first reading of the story. Notes about the genre and cultural perspective may be used during subsequent readings.

THE NAME OF THE TREE

a Bantu folk tale
retold by Celia Barker Lottridge

Think Aloud

[1] *I see the animals solved the problem of finding food, but now they have a new problem: they cannot reach the fruit. I wonder if they will find a way to work together to reach the food. Maybe they could stand on each other's backs.*

Once, long ago, in the land of the short grass, there was a great hunger. No rain fell, and no grass grew.

The ostrich, the gazelle, the giraffe, the monkey, the rabbit, the tortoise, the zebra, and all the other animals were hungry. They searched in the jungle, they searched by the river, they searched on the great flat <u>plain</u>, but they could find nothing to eat.

At last all the animals gathered together and they said, "Let us go together across the great flat plain until we come to something we can eat."

And so all the animals, except for the lion, who was king and lived in the jungle, walked across the flat, empty land. They walked and walked. After many days, they saw a small bump on the edge of the flat land.

Then they saw that the small bump was a tree.

And the tree was very tall.

And the tree had fruit on it, such fruit as they had never seen before.

It was as red as <u>pomegranates</u>, as yellow as bananas, as green as melons, as purple as plums, as orange as mangos, and it smelled like all the fruits of the world.

But the tree was so tall and the branches so high that even the giraffe couldn't reach the fruit. And the trunk was so smooth that even the monkey couldn't climb the tree.[1]

The animals sat on the ground and cried because the fruit smelled so good and they were so hungry.

At last, when they were too tired to cry any longer, a very old tortoise spoke.

"O animals," she said, "my great-great-great-grandmother told me a story about a wonderful tree. The fruit of that tree was delicious and good to eat. But it could be reached only by those who knew the name of the tree."

The animals cried out, "But who can tell us the name of the tree?"

The very old tortoise answered, "The king knows. We must send someone to ask him."

"I will go," said the gazelle. "I am the fastest runner of us all." And that was true.

So the gazelle started out across the great flat plain. He ran like an arrow shot from a bow, and as he ran he thought, "How lucky the animals are that I am willing to go to the king. No one can run as fast as I."

Indeed, it was not long before the gazelle reached the jungle and the place by the river where the king lived.

The king was sitting with his tail neatly wrapped around him. Every hair in his golden coat lay smooth and shining. He spoke kindly to the gazelle. "What do you wish of me," he said.

"O great king," said the gazelle, "all the animals are hungry and we have found a tree filled with wonderful fruit. But we cannot eat the fruit until we know the name of the tree."

"I will tell you," said the lion, "but you must remember, for I don't want to have to tell anyone else. The name of the tree is Ungalli."

"Ungalli," said the gazelle. "I will run as fast as the wind and I will reach the tree before I can possibly forget."

The gazelle thanked the king and began to run through the jungle and across the great flat plain. He thought about how happy all the animals would be, and how they would thank him and be grateful to him. He thought about this so hard that he did not see a rabbit hole that lay in his path, not far from where the animals were waiting. He stepped in it and went head over hoofs over head over hoofs. He landed in a heap at the foot of the tree.

"What is the name of the tree?" shouted the animals.

The gazelle shook his head. He shook it again. But the name was gone. "I can't remember," he whispered.

The animals groaned. "We will have to send someone else," they said. "Someone who will not forget."

"I will go," said the elephant. "I never forget anything."

The animals nodded, for this was true. And so the elephant strode off across the great flat plain.

"I will not forget," she said to herself. "I can remember anything I choose to. Even the names of all my cousins." The elephant had hundreds of cousins. "Or the names of all the stars in the sky."

When the elephant arrived at the edge of the river, the king was sitting in his usual place, but the end of his tail was twitching and his fur was ruffled.

"What do you want," he growled.

"O king," said the elephant, "all the animals are hungry . . ."

"I know," said the lion, "and you want to know the name of the tree with the wonderful fruit. I will tell you, but don't you forget because I absolutely will not tell anyone else. The name of the tree is Ungalli."

"I will not forget," said the elephant <u>haughtily</u>. "I never forget anything." And she turned and began to make her way out of the jungle.

"Forget," she grumbled to herself. "Me, forget! Why, I can remember the names of all the trees in this jungle." And she began to name them. When she had finished the jungle trees, she went on to all the other trees in Africa. She was just starting on the trees of the rest of the world when she happened to step in the very rabbit hole that had tripped the gazelle. Her foot fitted exactly into the hole, so exactly that she couldn't get it out.

The animals waiting under the tree saw the elephant and ran toward her calling, "What is the name of the tree?"

The elephant pulled and tugged and pulled and tugged, and at last with a great *pop* her foot came out of the hole.

"I can't remember," she said crossly, "and I don't care.[2] That tree has caused far too much trouble already."

The animals didn't even groan. They were too tired and too hungry.

After a long time a very young tortoise spoke.

"O animals," he said, "I will go and find out the name of the tree."

"You!" said the animals. "But you are so young and you are so small and you are so slow."

"Yes," said the very young tortoise. "But I know how to remember. I learned from my great-great-great-grandmother, the one who told you about the tree."

The animals had nothing to say. And the little tortoise was already on his way. It is true that he was slow. But by putting one short leg ahead of the other he crossed the great flat plain, went through the jungle, and arrived at the place by the river where the king lived.

The king was not sitting in his usual place. He was pacing up and down the bank of the river, waving his tail. His fur was standing on end.

Think Aloud

[2] *This is the second animal that has forgotten the name of the tree. I think the author is trying to show that both animals forgot the name of the tree because they filled their heads with other thoughts instead of concentrating on the name of the tree.*

When he saw the very young tortoise, he roared, "If you have come to ask me the name of the tree, go home. I have told the gazelle and I have told the elephant that the name of the tree is Ungalli, and I will *not* tell you."

The very young tortoise nodded his head politely. He turned and began to walk out of the jungle.

As he walked he said, "Ungalli, Ungalli, the name of the tree is Ungalli. Ungalli, Ungalli, the name of the tree is Ungalli."

And he went on saying it as he crossed the great flat plain. "Ungalli, Ungalli, the name of the tree is Ungalli."

And he never stopped saying it, even when he got tired, even when he got thirsty. Because that is what his great-great-great-grandmother had told him to do. Even when he fell right to the bottom of that same rabbit hole, the very young tortoise just climbed out saying, "Ungalli, Ungalli, the name of the tree is Ungalli."[3]

None of the animals saw him coming. They were sitting under the tree, looking at the ground. The very young tortoise walked straight up to the foot of the tree and said in a loud voice, "The name of the tree is Ungalli!"

The animals looked up.

They saw the branches of the tree bend down so low that they could reach the wonderful fruit that was as red as pomegranates, as yellow as bananas, as green as melons, as purple as plums, and as orange as mangos, and smelled like all the fruits of the world.

The animals ate. They ate until they could eat no more. And then they lifted the very young tortoise high in the air and marched around the tree chanting, "Ungalli, Ungalli, the name of the tree is Ungalli," because they did not want to forget. And they never did.

Think Aloud

[3] *I made a connection here with my own way of remembering things. I repeat words that I want to remember, too. I also use rhythm to remember numbers, poems, or songs. I think the tortoise in this story will be able to do what the others could not because he knows how to remember things.*

After Reading

Retell the Story: Have students create simple flat animal masks with African designs and use them to retell the story.

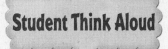

Use Copying Master number 2 to prompt students to share a connection they made in the story.

"I made a connection when . . ."

Cultural Perspectives

There are many versions of this folk tale, but the lesson is the same. In each version, speaking animals attempt to bring the name of the tree back to the rest of the animals and the proud animals always fail.

Think and Respond

1. According to the gazelle and the elephant, why will they succeed in finding out the name of the tree? Why do the animals think the tortoise won't succeed? *Possible responses: The gazelle is a fast runner and the elephant has a good memory. The other animals think the young tortoise is too small and slow to complete the task.* **Analytical**

2. What similarities do you see between the folk tales "The Name of the Tree" and "Frog and Locust"? *Possible responses: Both stories feature animals as main characters. Both stories are about animals who are trying to stay alive. Both stories show animals working together to solve a problem.* **Genre**

3. What message do you think the author wants to share with readers? *Possible responses: Even someone who is young, small, and slow can achieve a goal. Being persistent and focused will help you accomplish a difficult task. Pride goeth before a fall.* **Author's Purpose**

Nests and How They Are Built
by Phyllis Goldman

Genre: Informational Nonfiction Article

Comprehension Strategy: Summarize

Think-Aloud Copying Master number 4

Before Reading

Genre: Tell students you will read aloud a nonfiction article. Invite them to recall other nonfiction articles they have heard or read, such as "The Wolves of Winter." Remind students that the purpose of this type of text is to inform the reader about a topic. A nonfiction article includes facts and other information to help the reader understand the topic.

Expand Vocabulary: Introduce the following words before reading:

> *tend:* take care of
>
> *territory:* an area of land
>
> *exact:* specific
>
> *elaborate:* fancy; very complex

Set a Purpose for Reading: Invite students to listen to find out the steps birds take to build nests.

During Reading

Use the comprehension Think Alouds during the first reading of the story. Notes about the genre and cultural perspective may be used during subsequent readings.

Think Aloud

[1] *I had no idea that one bird chooses the area where the nest is built and the other bird chooses exactly where to build the nest. That is an interesting piece of information.*

Think Aloud

[2] *I figured out that "without being taught" is the definition of the word* instinctively *because it comes directly after the word. I think the author does this to help me understand a difficult word.*

Nests and How They Are Built

by Phyllis Goldman

Like many animals and insects, birds build *nests* as homes. These *nests* are found in different areas called habitats, which include open fields and wooded areas.

The nest provides a place for the bird to lay eggs and later feed and <u>tend</u> to baby birds. It also offers protection to the mother while she is guarding her eggs.

Most male birds choose the <u>territory</u> in which the nest will be *built*. The female bird then decides the <u>exact</u> location and begins building.[1]

Using only her bill and feet, the bird gathers grass, twigs, leaves and other small materials. It then weaves these materials into a strong and safe home. The female often lines the inside of the nest with mud, rotten wood; and feathers. It then uses its saliva to pack down the mud for a smooth surface.

Birds travel many times to and from the nest to carry materials. The bird instinctively (without being taught) builds an <u>elaborate</u> nest for its young.[2]

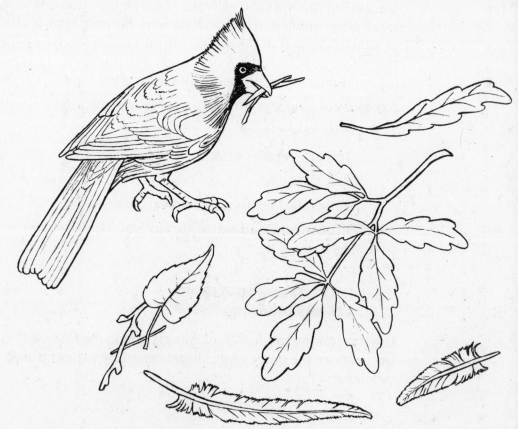

 **After Reading**

Take Notes: Have students summarize the most important information they learned in the article. Ask one student to paraphrase each step as a partner draws it, retelling the information through pictures.

Student Think Aloud

Use Copying Master number 4 to prompt students to discuss a word or idea they figured out using context clues or prior knowledge.

"I figured out _____ because _____."

Cultural Perspective

In China, some people consider a bird's nest a gourmet meal. Birds called swiflets make their nests in caves using seaweed and their own saliva. People soak the nests in water and then use tweezers to pull out any extra material. The nests can be served in a soup with chicken or ham, or they can be boiled with water and rock sugar and served as a dessert.

Think and Respond

1. What other information could the author have included to tell the reader more about the topic? *Possible responses: how birds choose the location for a nest; how birds find their way back to the nest when they are looking for building materials; how long it takes to build the nest.* **Critical**

2. What details does the author use to describe how birds build nests? *Possible responses: Birds use grass, twigs, and leaves to build the nest. Birds line the nest with mud, rotten wood, and feathers. Birds only use their bill and feet to make the nest. Birds use saliva to pack down the mud.* **Genre**

3. For what kind of reader do you think the author wrote this article? *Possible responses: someone who wants to know more about how birds build nest; someone who is not an expert about birds and wants basic information about building nests.* **Author's Purpose**

The Town That Moved

by Mary Jane Finsand

Genre: Nonfiction

Comprehension Strategy: Analyze Text Structure

Think-Aloud Copying Master number 5

Before Reading

Genre: Tell students you will read aloud a nonfiction informational selection. Remind them that all the information in a nonfiction selection is true and includes real people and events. Hibbing is located in Minnesota and the events described in this selection took place in 1919.

Expand Vocabulary: Introduce the following words before reading:

ore: a rock or mineral that contains metal

mine: a pit in the ground from which ore is taken

cranes: machines used for moving heavy objects

Set a Purpose for Reading: Invite students to listen to find out just how the people of Hibbing were able to move their town.

During Reading

Use the comprehension Think Alouds during the first reading of the story. The genre note may be used during subsequent readings.

The Town That Moved

by Mary Jane Finsand

Hibbing became famous for its rich iron ore. The town grew and grew. Everyone who lived there was very proud of Hibbing. They wanted to make it a beautiful city. They built fancy theaters and lovely parks and fine houses. They started excellent schools for their children, and they took wonderful care of their town.[1] Then one day the mine owners made a discovery: THE VERY BEST IRON ORE WAS RIGHT BENEATH THE TOWN OF HIBBING!

The people of Hibbing would have to move. If they didn't, the mines would have to be shut down. The miners would be out of work. Soon the other businesses would have to close down too. The people of Hibbing were very upset. They had worked so hard to build their beautiful town. How could they leave it? How could they watch it be torn down to make way for new mines?

"Where will we go?" they asked. "We will build you a new town," said the mine owners. "But what about our fine homes and our fancy theaters and our beautiful hotels?" the people asked. The mine owners thought and thought, and finally they came up with a solution.

"We will move your homes!" they said. "We will move the whole town!" It sounded like a wonderful idea. But how on earth would they do it?[2] The mine owners and the people sat down together to think and talk.

"We have horses and tractors," said one man. "Maybe we could pull the buildings."

"They will break into pieces. We need wheels or something," said the mayor.

"Wheels are a problem," said the mine owners. "Most of our wheels are just not large or strong enough to move a building."

"Well," said someone else, "we certainly have lots of trees. We could cut them down, then make them smooth and roll our houses on them."

"That's it!" everyone cried.

So the mine owners and the people began to get ready for moving day. They separated all the buildings from their basements. Then they dug new basements for all those buildings. They chopped down trees. Then they cut away branches.

Genre Study

Nonfiction: The writer gives a step-by-step account of how the hotel was moved. This kind of detailed description helps readers visualize this incredible event.

They made the logs smooth. People all over the world heard about Hibbing's plan to move. "Impossible!" they said. One big city newspaper wrote: "HIBBING GONE CRAZY!"

No one believed that the people of Hibbing could move their whole town. Finally moving day arrived. The Hibbing Hotel would be the first building moved. The miners attached large chains and ropes to <u>cranes</u> from the mine. The cranes would be powered by steam engines. Then the chains were wrapped over and under the Hibbing Hotel.

Slowly the cranes lifted the hotel. Then they swung it over and lowered it gently onto a log roller. Next, ropes and straps were wrapped around the hotel, then attached to horses up front. "Giddap! Giddap!" shouted the horse drivers. The horses started forward. Slowly the Hibbing Hotel rolled down the street. As soon as the back log rolled out from under the building, people grabbed it. They strapped it to a horse and pulled it up to the front. Then they slid it underneath again.

After the Hibbing Hotel was moved, they moved the Oliver Clubhouse. The Oliver was so big, it had to be cut in two parts to move it.

Down the street the buildings rolled to their new locations. Day in and day out, the people of Hibbing worked to save their beautiful town.[3] At last all the business buildings had been moved. Next would come the houses.

"What should we do with our furniture?" the women asked.

"And our toys and clothes," said the children.

"Leave everything in the houses," they were told. "And you can ride in your houses too."

The very next day the first house was lifted onto logs. Down the street it came. A log was placed up front. Then a log rolled out back. That log was placed up front, and another log rolled out back.

And so it went until, one after another, 186 houses had been moved. The people of Hibbing had done it! They had moved their whole town!

Think Aloud

[3] *I noticed that the author stated the problem first and then explains exactly how the townspeople solved the problem.*

After Reading

Take Notes: Have students produce a variety of written responses, some of which reflect on self as reader and writer. Ask students to show the versions they write.

Student Think Aloud

Use Copying Master number 5 to prompt students to discuss descriptive details or word choices the writer uses to explain how the town was moved.

"I noticed the author . . ."

Cultural Perspectives

Have students evaluate this story based on the culture and the time period. What if Hibbing needed to be moved today?

Think and Respond

1. Why do you think the people of Hibbing worked so hard to save their town rather than build a new one in a different location? *Possible responses: The people had worked hard to create their town and make it a nice place to live. They did not want to destroy all the beautiful buildings.* **Analytical**

2. What do you notice about the quotations in this selection? Why do you think the individual speakers are not identified by name? *Possible responses: The writer does not include the name of the person who says each quotation. She does this because it is not necessary for readers to know exactly who said what. It is more important to give a sense of how the people reacted to the idea of moving the town.* **Genre**

3. Why do you think Mary Jane Finsand chose to write about Hibbing? *Possible response: She thought readers would enjoy a story of how people were able to move a whole town.* **Author's Purpose**

Dolphin Play

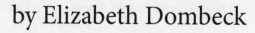

by Elizabeth Dombeck

Genre: Nonfiction Article

Comprehension Strategy: Monitor Comprehension

Think-Aloud Copying Master number 7

Before Reading

Genre: Tell students they will listen to a nonfiction article in which the author describes her own personal experiences about a topic. Explain that although the writer uses first person, including the words *I*, *me*, and *my*, her purpose is not to tell a story but to relate actual events.

Expand Vocabulary: Introduce these words before reading:

> *enriching:* stimulating
>
> *nudged:* pushed gently
>
> *flinched:* moved back quickly in fear
>
> *echolocation:* sound waves emitted by some animals to locate objects

Set a Purpose for Reading: Have students listen for description of dolphin play and author's word choice, including sensory details.

During Reading

Use the comprehension Think Alouds during the first reading of the story. Notes about the genre and cultural perspective may be used during subsequent readings.

Dolphin Play

by Elizabeth Dombeck

Dolphins are playful animals. In the wild, it is not uncommon to see dolphins chasing a sea turtle, playing with a piece of driftwood, or frolicking with each other. In zoos, it is up to the keepers to provide an <u>enriching</u> environment for the dolphins. When I worked as a dolphin keeper, one of my biggest challenges was to invent new toys for the dolphins.

I knew the dolphins loved to play with balls. But I wanted to make the balls interesting. I came up with jingle balls! I put different-size, jingle bells inside of a basketball. When I threw the ball into the pool, one of the dolphins immediately <u>nudged</u> the ball with his nose. Then he <u>flinched</u> and swam to the bottom of the pool. He stayed there for a while staring at the ball. He appeared afraid of the ball, and I thought my great idea was a flop. Then I realized that Nemo was using his <u>echolocation</u> on the ball!

I had such fun with the jingle ball that I wanted to do more. While shopping at a toy store, I stumbled across some giant balls. I wondered if the dolphins would play with them or be afraid of them. There was only one way to find out.

Within seconds of putting the balls into the water, seven dolphins surfaced and surrounded the balls. Soon balls were flying everywhere. The dolphins were pushing the balls with their snouts and whacking them with their tails.[1] One dolphin even figured out how to hit the ball outside of the pool and have it bounce back in. She would swim upside down beneath the ball and whack it with her tail. The ball would fly out of the water, bounce off the bleachers, and sail back into the water.

From then on, when the dolphins saw me rolling the balls toward the pool, they would all crowd around, as if saying, "Throw it to me."

Next, I wanted to do something for the baby dolphins. I decided to see if little dolphins would like bubbles as much as little children. The next day, I brought a jar of bubbles to work. I blew bubbles out over the pool.[2] The dolphins surfaced quickly to see what was floating above the surface of the water. The adults lost interest quickly, but the little ones chirped and whistled as bubbles floated down around them.

Genre Study

Nonfiction Article: The writer provides background information on how dolphins play in the wild. Then she explains how she helped dolphins play in a zoo.

Think Aloud

[1] *I am able to picture in my mind all the dolphins playing with the balls. It must have been amusing and exciting to see the dolphins enjoying their new toys.*

Think Aloud

[2] *I can use visualization of the author's descriptions to help monitor my comprehension.*

Body surfing is a popular pastime for the dolphins. Instead of surfing on waves, the dolphins surfed on a large, foam mat. They'd leap from the water and land on the mat. Then the mat would sail forward, taking the dolphins for a ride.[3]

Sometimes, I would put pieces of fish and ice cubes on the mat. The dolphins always enjoyed their snack. One of the dolphins loved ice cubes so much that once he ate a 10-pound bag all by himself.

Think Aloud

[3]*This was mostly about how the author came up with new toys for the dolphins.*

After Reading

Take Notes: Have students make a Venn diagram to show what they learned from the selection about dolphin activities in the wild and in a zoo. Have them label one circle *Wild*, the other circle *Zoo*, and the overlapping section *Both*. Discuss what students learned from the article and the quality of the text based on its usefulness.

Student Think Aloud

Use Copying Master number 7 to prompt students to tell what a part of the story was mostly about.

"This was mostly about ..."

Cultural Perspectives

International Dolphin Watch works to protect dolphins in the wild and study interactions between humans and dolphins. Through its research efforts, this organization has found human and dolphin interactions especially helpful for people with disabilities such as cerebral palsy, Down's syndrome, and autism.

Think and Respond

1. Why do you think the writer felt it was important to create toys for the dolphins? *Possible responses: The writer says that dolphins are animals that like to play. The dolphins in the zoo needed toys because they could not do the same things they do in the ocean.* **Analytical**

2. What descriptive details does the writer use to help readers visualize what she is describing? *Possible responses: She describes the dolphins' movements and how they reacted to each toy. She describes the different objects used as toys.* **Genre**

3. Why do you think Elizabeth Dombeck chose to write about the dolphins under her care? *Possible responses: It is clear she enjoys working with the dolphins, so she is writing about a topic she knows well. She thinks that readers would be interested to learn about the different things the dolphins do just for fun.* **Author's Purpose**

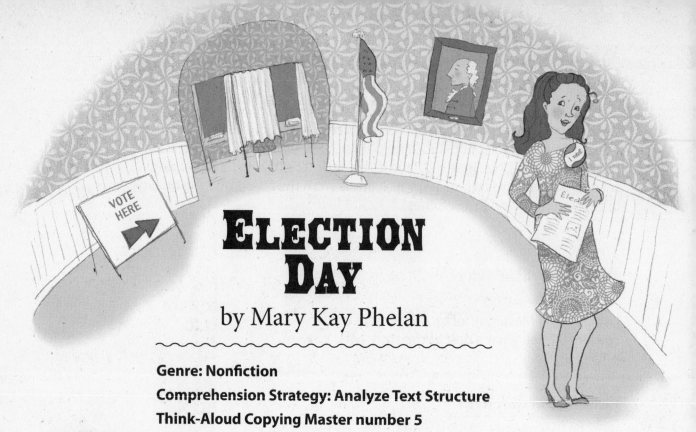

ELECTION DAY

by Mary Kay Phelan

Genre: Nonfiction

Comprehension Strategy: Analyze Text Structure

Think-Aloud Copying Master number 5

 Before Reading

Genre: Tell students they will listen to a nonfiction selection that explains the importance and historical background of Election Day. Remind students that a nonfiction text is meant to inform, so it includes factual information as well as interesting supporting details to help readers better understand the topic.

Expand Vocabulary: Introduce the following words and phrases before reading:

> *polling places:* locations where people go to vote
>
> *stream into:* enter at a constant pace
>
> *ballots:* paper sheets on which voters mark their choices
>
> *customs:* ways of doing things

Set a Purpose for Reading: Have students listen for descriptions of how voting methods have changed over the years.

 **During Reading**

Use the comprehension Think Alouds during the first reading of the story. Notes about the genre and cultural perspective may be used during subsequent readings.

ELECTION DAY

by Mary Kay Phelan

In the fall people all over the United States look forward to Election Day. It is always celebrated on the first Tuesday after the first Monday in November.

On this holiday we show how proud we are to live in a free country.

Election Day is different from all other American holidays. Some holidays celebrate something that happened long ago. Others honor an important person's birthday. But Election Day is a holiday when we plan for the future.[1]

On Election Day we vote for the men and women who will govern our towns, our counties, our states, and our nation.

Plans for Election Day begin many weeks ahead of time. The people who want to be elected are called candidates. They make speeches. They write letters to the voters. They tell everyone what they will do if they are elected.

Then on Election Day the voters decide which candidates they want.

On Election Day people vote at polling places. Sometimes the polling place is a school or a church. In some towns it may be a firehouse, a store, or a courthouse.

All day long people stream into the polling places. Each person goes into a little booth all alone. His [or her] vote is secret.

Some people vote for one person. Some vote for another. Because this is a free country, no one tells us how to vote. We choose the candidate we think will do the best job.

After the polling places close, the votes are counted. Soon everyone knows who has won the election. . . .

Americans . . . have always wanted the freedom to vote for the people who are to govern them. That is one of the reasons why the first colonists came to America from England.

As early as 1620 the settlers of Plymouth, Massachusetts, held elections for a governor. People voted by raising their hands in a public meeting. Then in 1634 the people of the Massachusetts Bay Colony tried something new. They used paper ballots and voted in secret. . . .[2]

Think Aloud

[1] *I think this part is important because I never thought of Election Day as a holiday. I think of a holiday as a day off from school or a day when you celebrate something. Now I see that Election Day is an important day because when we vote we are choosing the people we want for our government.*

Think Aloud

[2] *I notice the author used a date to make a transition from the present to a time in the past. This part of the article is mostly about how the first settlers voted. I can compare this to how we vote today.*

Sometimes the early settlers used kernels of corn and Indian beans for voting. When a man dropped a white kernel of corn into the ballot box, he was voting for the candidate. If he used a black bean, he was voting against the candidate.

Not all the colonies used paper ballots or corn and beans for voting. Election Day in the colonies of New York, New Jersey, Maryland, Virginia, and Georgia was very different. At each polling place the man in charge of the election had a large book. The names of the candidates were written in the book.

When the voter arrived, he announced in a loud voice the men for whom he wished to vote. His choices were recorded in the book. The candidates rose and bowed in thanks. Their friends clapped. . . .

Many of the colonists who voted [this way] came from England. They were voting the way people in England had voted for hundreds of years.

But the voice vote was not secret. Everyone knew how a man voted. Sometimes people were afraid to vote as they really wished.

[After the Declaration of Independence in 1776] the colonies were independent of England. Because they did not want to keep the English <u>customs</u>, the ways of voting were changed. One by one, the new states adopted paper ballots for their elections. . . .[3]

Election Day is one of our most exciting holidays. Even if you cannot vote yet, you can share in the excitement. You can listen to the candidates. You can learn what they hope to do if they are elected.

As long as Americans can vote for whom they wish, our country will always be strong and free. The future of the United States depends on its Election Days.

[3]*I heard the word* adopted. *I know that* adopted *is a verb that can mean when a family brings a child that has no parents into their home. That meaning does not make sense here. It says that the ways of voting changed. I think* adopted *in this sentence means "started using." So the sentence is saying that states started using paper ballots for voting.*

After Reading

Take Notes: Ask students to write a one-paragraph summary of the selection. Remind them that a summary includes only the most important information. Have students trade papers with a partner and compare which information they included in their summaries.

Student Think Aloud

Use Copying Master number 5 to prompt students to discuss paragraphs in the story and what they were mostly about.

"I noticed the author used . . ."

Cultural Perspective

Voting methods in America have come a long way since the first settlers voted by raising their hands. Today people in many states touch a computer screen to vote electronically. In other states voters shade in a box to indicate their choice or use a machine to punch a hole next to their choice. However, there are some states that still use paper ballots. Have students discuss the cultures and times reflected in the article and other changes across time.

Think and Respond

1. Why did states eventually decide to use paper ballots for their elections? *Possible responses: People wanted their vote to be secret. The states broke away from England and did not want to continue doing things the way the English did them.* **Analytical**

2. Why do you think the author describes several different ways people in America used to vote? *Possible responses: These ways show how things have changed since 1620. It is interesting to learn about the different ways people used to vote. She shows why people wanted a new voting method.* **Genre**

3. What message do you think Mary Kay Phelan wants to share with her readers? *Possible response: Election Day is an important holiday that everyone can be involved in, even if you cannot yet vote.* **Author's Purpose**

The Giant Jam Sandwich

by John Vernon Lord and Janet Burroway

Genre: Rhyming Poem

Poetic Element: Onomatopoeia

Comprehension Strategy: Ask Questions

Think-Aloud Copying Master number 1

Before Reading

Genre: Remind students that a rhyming poem contains a rhyming pattern. Tell them to listen for rhyming words as you read aloud the poem. Explain that this is a narrative poem because it tells a story. Like a narrative story, it includes characters, a setting, dialogue, and a problem and solution.

Expand Vocabulary: Introduce the following words and phrases before reading:

pate: the top of the head

yeast: an ingredient used to make bread dough rise

mill: a building where grain is ground into flour

drew up: drove up, arrived

Set a Purpose for Reading: Invite students to listen for enjoyment and for the poets' use of onomatopoeia.

During Reading

Read with expression, noting the use of italics, questions, exclamations, and onomatopoeia. Read through the poem the first time without interruptions. Then reread, pausing to draw students' attention to the comprehension Think Aloud and genre note.

The Giant Jam Sandwich

by John Vernon Lord and Janet Burroway

One hot summer in Itching Down,
Four million wasps flew into town.
They drove the picnickers away,
They chased the farmers from their hay,
They stung Lord Swell on his fat bald <u>pate</u>,
They dived and hummed and buzzed and ate,
And the noisy, nasty nuisance grew
Till the villagers cried, "What *can* we *do*?"

So they called a meeting in the village hall,
And Mayor Muddlenut asked them all,
"What *can* we *do*?" And they said, "Good question!"
But nobody had a good suggestion.

Then Bap the Baker leaped to his feet
And cried, "What do wasps like best to eat?
Strawberry jam! Now wait a minute!
If we made a giant sandwich we could trap them in it!"[1]
The gentlemen cheered, the ladies squealed,
And Farmer Seed said, "Use my field."

Bap gave instructions for the making of the dough.
"Mix flour from above and <u>yeast</u> from below.
Salt from the seaside, water from the spout.
Now thump it! Bump it! Bang it about!"

While they were working, and working hard,
Some more made a tablecloth out in the yard.
When they were done, the dough was left to rise
Till the loaf was a mountain in shape and size!

They hitched it up, with a bit of fuss,
To tractors, cars and the village bus,
And took it to the oven they had made on the hill—
Fifty cookers in an old brick <u>mill</u>.

Genre Study

Onomatopoeia: The poets use onomatopoeia, words that sound like the action or thing they describe. Words such as *hummed* and *buzzed* are more vivid because they sound like what they mean.

Think Aloud

[1]*I noticed the poets use exaggeration to make the poem humorous. How in the world could the people make a sandwich big enough to trap four million wasps? The poets also use humor in the characters' names, such as Mayor Muddlenut and Bap the Baker.*

For hours and hours they let it cook.
It swelled inside till the windows shook.
It was piping hot when they took it out,
And the villagers raised a mighty shout.
"Isn't it crusty, Aren't we clever!"
But the wasps were just as bad as ever.

The loaf was left to cool, and then
The people watched while six strong men
Took a great big saw and sliced right through.
Everybody clapped, and they cut slice two.

The village bus, they all agreed,
Would spoil the fields of Farmer Seed,
So eight fine horses pulled the bread
To where the picnic cloth was spread.[2]
A truck drew up and dumped out butter,
And they spread it out with a flap and a flutter.
Spoons and spades! Slap and slam!
And they did the same with the strawberry jam.

Meanwhile, high above the field,
Six flying machines whirred and wheeled,
Ready for the wasps to take the bait.
And then there was nothing to do but wait.

Suddenly the sky was humming!
All four million wasps were coming!
They smelled that jam, they dived and struck!
And they ate so much that they all got stuck.

The other slice came down—kersplat!—
On top of the wasps, and that was that.
There were only three that got away,
And where they are now I cannot say.

Think Aloud

[2]*I wonder how they are going to get the bread to Farmer Seed's field? Maybe they will put it on a truck.*

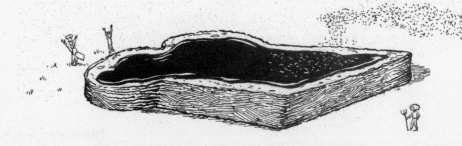

Set a Purpose for Rereading: Once you have read aloud the poem for students' enjoyment, reread it for the purpose of having students identify the rhyme scheme. Then ask students to write their own humorous poems, using poetic elements of exaggeration, rhyme, and onomatopoeia.

Student Think Aloud

Use Copying Master number 1 to prompt students to share something they noticed in the poem.

"I wonder . . ."

Think and Respond

1. How do the poets create humor in the poem? *Possible responses: They give people funny names like Mayor Muddlenut. They use exaggeration by making the sandwich big enough to trap four million wasps.* **Analytical**

2. What examples of onomatopoeia does the poem include? *Possible responses: hummed, buzzed, thump, bump, bang, slap, slam, whirred, kersplat.* **Genre**

3. Why do people enjoy hearing poems like this one? *Possible response: It makes them laugh because of the humor and exaggeration. After all, the authors' purpose is to entertain.* **Author's Purpose**

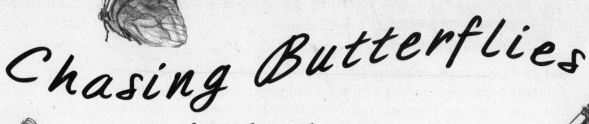

Chasing Butterflies

by Yuliya Chernova

Genre: Nonfiction Article

Comprehension Strategy: Monitor Comprehension

Think-Aloud Copying Master number 6

Before Reading

Genre: Tell students they will listen to a nonfiction article about a man who studies butterflies. Guide students to discuss the purpose of this type of selection (to inform) and the kind of information they would expect to learn from it (facts about butterflies and the people who study them).

Expand Vocabulary: Introduce the following words before reading to help students better understand the article:

> *entomologists:* scientists who study insects
>
> *pursuit:* activity
>
> *elusive:* hard to find
>
> *field guide:* a book that shows pictures of and gives information about the different species of a type of animal

Set a Purpose for Reading: Invite students to listen to find out what the title means.

During Reading

Use the comprehension Think Alouds during the first reading of the story. Notes about the genre and cultural perspective may be used during subsequent readings.

Genre Study

Nonfiction Article: The writer provides the definition and pronunciation of *lepidopterist*, a difficult word that is important to understanding the article.

Chasing Butterflies

by Yuliya Chernova

"Butterflies spoke to me," recalls Jeffrey Glassberg. As a 5-year-old, he started to keep lists of butterflies he spotted in his backyard in Long Island, New York. Now chasing butterflies has become his daily work. He is a lepidopterist (lep-eh-dop-teh-rist)—a scientist who studies moths and butterflies.

"No one actually calls himself a lepidopterist," says Glassberg, who is a field butterfly expert and president of the North American Butterfly Association. "We're biologists or entomologists."

Glassberg studies the distribution of 600 butterfly species in North America.[1] But he doesn't simply examine specimens under a microscope. This scientist chases his fluttering subjects all over the U.S., Canada and Mexico. Glassberg visits mountain meadows and draws maps that show where species live and their travel patterns. He also develops ways to tell similar species apart. "By their eye-color—that's a new technique," he says.

Butterfly chasing might sound like a gentle pursuit, but it has risks. Glassberg has taken a few tumbles chasing elusive butterflies. "Once I ended up 20 feet below a cliff," he recalls.

Glassberg has degrees in environmental engineering, biology and law. He studied law to learn how to protect butterflies from habitat loss caused by construction. "I thought butterflies might need a friend," he explains.

His tips for kids who want to be amateur lepidopterists: During warm months, go to a park and slowly approach butterflies. Use a field guide to identify what kind you see. "Studying butterflies is an activity that is good for the planet and a lot of fun," says Glassberg. Plus, "you are always outside in warm weather. What's not to like about that?"[2]

"Butterflies are beautiful, so are the places where they live," says Glassberg.

Think Aloud

[1] *I wonder what the author means here when she uses the word* distribution. *She says Glassberg chases butterflies all over the United States, Canada, and Mexico. She also says he studies their travel patterns. So I think* distribution *means where the butterflies live and where they travel.*

Think Aloud

[2] *At first I thought chasing butterflies was just a hobby people did in their backyard and then I found out from this article that it can actually be a job!*

Take Notes: Have students list science-related terms and other new words they learned from the article.

Student Think Aloud

Use Copying Master number 6 to prompt students to share an opinion or conclusion that changed after they read the article.

"At first I thought _____ and then I found out _____."

Cultural Perspective

There are about 20,000 species of butterflies in the world. Many butterflies migrate according to the seasons. Butterflies that cannot survive the cold winter in Canada and the northern United States fly south to the southern states and Mexico and then return in the summer.

Think and Respond

1. What do you think Jeffrey Glassberg means when he says "Butterflies spoke to me"? *Possible response: I think he means that butterflies were very interesting to him. Perhaps he was so interested in them he felt that they were calling him to come study them.* **Critical**

2. Why do you think the writer includes tips for kids who want to study butterflies? *Possible response: Maybe reading about all the things Jeffrey Glassberg does as a lepidopterist will make other people interested in studying butterflies.* **Genre**

3. Why do you think Yuliya Chernova chose to write about Jeffrey Glassberg? *Possible response: She wants to inform people that chasing butterflies can start as a hobby and become an exciting job.* **Author's Purpose**

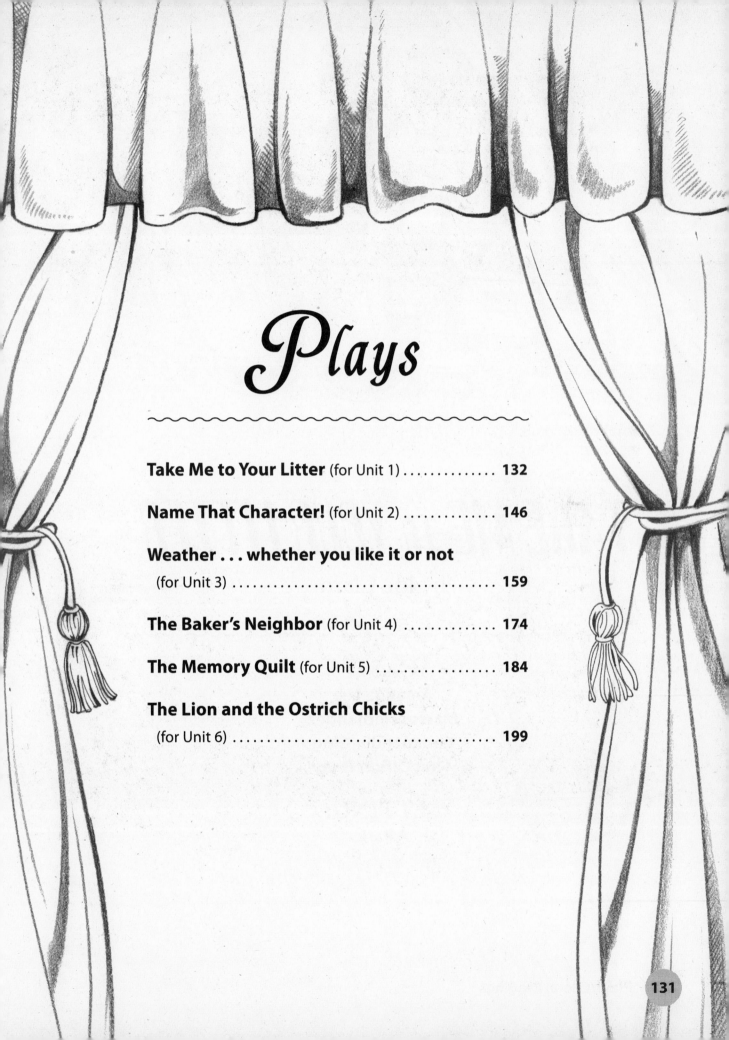

Plays

TAKE ME TO YOUR LITTER

by Joe Claro

CAST:
Amanda Lee
Marcos Hernandez
Commander Glug
First Officer Blug

SETTING:
A Park

Amanda: Hi, Marcos. What's happening?

Marcos: Oh hi, Amanda, Not much, I guess. I'm supposed to meet my cub scout group over by the entrance to the park.

Amanda: Are you going on a hike or something?

Marcos: Nope. I sure wish we were. Instead, we're supposed to sort cans at the recycling center for a couple of hours.

Amanda: What a way to spend a Saturday!

Marcos: My feelings exactly. Hey . . . what's that noise? Do you hear something strange?

Amanda: Yeah, it sounds like a swarm of bees.

Marcos: It's too loud for bees. It seems to be coming from the sky. Can you see anything up there?

Amanda: Just a few clouds and a lot of blue sky. Wait! I think I do see something!

Marcos: Me, too! It looks like a gigantic metal triangle!

Amanda: Look out, Marcos! It's coming closer!

Marcos: AND GETTING LOUDER EVERY SECOND!

Amanda: IT'S LANDING IN THE PARK!

Marcos: WHAT ON EARTH DO YOU THINK IT IS?

Amanda: IT DOESN'T LOOK LIKE ANYTHING ON EARTH! Shhh! The humming sound has finally stopped.

Marcos: It's so quiet. This is scary. What do you think is going on?

Amanda: Look, a door—or something—is opening. And someone—or something—is climbing out. I think we ought to get out of here!

Marcos: Wait a minute. Is . . . is that a person?

Amanda: I'm . . . not . . . sure. It looks kind of like a person. Two eyes and a mouth. And I guess that could be a nose.

Marcos: But where is the hair, and where are the ears?

Amanda: Look! There's a second one! I think we should go home!

Marcos: Wait! They've seen us. One of them is waving.

Amanda: Listen! It's speaking to us!

Marcos: What should we do?

Amanda: Shh! I'm trying to make out what it's saying.

Glug: Blim torp en karben?

Amanda: Blim torpen . . . what? Excuse me? Uh . . . I couldn't catch everything you said.

Glug: Oh, pardon me. My memory functions failed, and for a moment I forgot where I was. I requested you to give us directions.

Marcos: Directions? But who are you? Where did you come from?

Glug: Let me introduce myself. My name is Commander Glug. And this is my first officer, Blug. We arrived from the planet Fargone. Greetings!

Amanda: I don't believe this is happening!

Marcos: Me, either! But I don't think we're dreaming, do you?

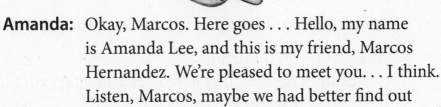

Amanda: Okay, Marcos. Here goes . . . Hello, my name is Amanda Lee, and this is my friend, Marcos Hernandez. We're pleased to meet you. . . I think. Listen, Marcos, maybe we had better find out what they want.

Marcos: I think you're right, Amanda. Maybe the best thing to do is to just ask. . . . Welcome, Commander Glug and First Officer Blug. What are you doing here?

Glug: We are attempting to locate the planet Earth. We're on a special mission.

Amanda: Well, you've reached your destination. This is Earth.

Glug: Did you hear that, Blug? We're in the correct place!

Blug: Yes, I heard it, Commander. And to think that you wanted to make a right turn at Venus. Who knows where we would be now if we had done that!

Glug: Come. Let us stretch our legs. I feel as if I've been sitting for a thousand years.

Amanda: Just how long have you been traveling?

Blug: By the way you measure time, I would say about a thousand years. But in our time, it is only about an hour and a half.

Glug: This certainly is a very desirable planet you two have here.

Amanda: I'm glad you like it, but it isn't exactly ours. We share it with a few billion other people.

Blug: Yes, we are aware of that.

Amanda: Oh? How do you know what the population of Earth is?

Blug: Our scientists have been studying your planet for many centuries.

Marcos: No kidding? Why?

Glug: Because Earth seems to have almost everything we require in a planet, we're seriously thinking of coming here to live.

Amanda: Really? What makes Earth such a perfect place for Fargonians?

Blug: Well, it is not a perfect place for us yet. But it is our opinion that it soon will be.

Glug: Amanda and Marcos, please don't misunderstand us. We're prepared to make a fair trade. We're willing to teach you earthlings things we know. In return, we hope you'll allow us to share your planet.

Marcos: What kinds of things can you teach us?

Blug: Many things. We can teach you how to travel to other galaxies. We know how to read one another's thoughts. And, of course, there is teleportation.

Amanda: What's teleportation?

Glug: That's the ability to travel instantly to any place on the planet.

Marcos: Wow, I would like that.

Amanda: Where do you plan to live when you move to Earth?

© Macmillan/McGraw–Hill

Blug: We are not sure. That is one of several things Commander Glug and I were sent to investigate. Today we will travel all over your planet to "check things out," as you earthlings say.

Marcos: Really? Can we come with you?

Blug: Hmmm. That I do not know. Our manual does not say anything about taking natives on board the ship.

Marcos: Please? We won't be any trouble. You might even find us helpful in answering some of your questions.

Glug: Well . . . there are no rules against inviting natives on board. I think we could make an exception, just this once.

Amanda: Terrific! When do we leave?

Glug: We'll leave immediately, Amanda. My stars and planets! You're both so tall! Please duck as you come on board our space vehicle. Now, let's see, if you two sit over there, you'll be able to see the view screens.

Blug: Fasten your seat belts and prepare for lift-off!

Amanda: I don't feel a thing.

Marcos: Neither do I, but we are moving. Amanda, look at that view screen! There's the park! It's getting smaller and smaller.

Amanda: Now all I see are the clouds.

Glug: Please make yourselves comfortable. In a few minutes we will reach our first destination.

Marcos: Commander Glug, can you explain why the Fargonians want to move to Earth?

Glug: We've looked all over the solar system. Earth is the planet that has most of the features we want.

Amanda: I agree it's a great planet. But exactly what features are you interested in?

Glug: Well, for example, look at view screen number two, on the wall. Do you see that beautiful mound of substances?

Marcos: You mean that garbage? Trash? Litter?

Blug: Litter! Ah-h-h, I've always loved the sound of that word. We want to see more and more litter! You earthlings are true geniuses at producing it.

Glug: Yes, on Fargone we have a saying, "Take me to your litter!"

Amanda: But litter is dirty and ugly. We've been trying to cut down on the amount of litter we produce. When litter mounts up, it has to be destroyed, and that can cause air pollution.

Glug: Air pollution? What's air pollution?

Marcos: It's dirt in the air. If you look at the air from a distance, you can see dark clouds caused by pollution.

Blug: Why, those are the dark clouds that attracted us to Earth in the first place! We have been fascinated by the lovely shapes you earthlings make out of your air.

Amanda: Wait. I don't think you understand. Air pollution is a bad thing. We are trying to do everything we can to get rid of those dark clouds.

Blug: I am shocked to hear that! What exactly are you earthlings doing?

Marcos: For one thing, we're buying cars that create less air pollution.

Amanda: And that isn't all. Businesses are trying to find ways to cut down on the pollution that factories produce.

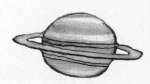

Marcos: And we're recycling some of our garbage, which means less of it has to be burned. That means less air pollution, too.

Blug: Do you hear that, Commander Glug? If they succeed, the lovely dark clouds may vanish forever.

Glug: That would be a terrible shame! It's a good thing that Earth has so many other features we're looking for.

Amanda: Like what?

Glug: If you observe screen number seven you can see part of the ocean. Even from space, our instruments could detect some beautiful rainbow patterns in the water.

Marcos: You mean oil slicks?

Glug: Oil slicks? That phrase has a nice ring to it. Back home, we call them wevver shoms.

Blug: Yes, and we create them all over our planet. We even have ships that do nothing but sail the Fargonian oceans, making wevver shoms in our water.

Glug: Everyone loves the rainbow designs. In fact, our Planetary TV System has a channel that shows nothing but wevver shoms day and night—all 785 days a year.

Blug: It is called the Wevver Channel.

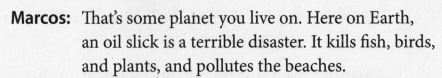

Marcos: That's some planet you live on. Here on Earth, an oil slick is a terrible disaster. It kills fish, birds, and plants, and pollutes the beaches.

Amanda: Oil slicks make the water unsafe for people, too. We can't drink it or swim in it.

Glug: Still, you must admit wevver shoms are beautiful to look at.

Marcos: Let's just say that's a matter of opinion. Anyway, we're fighting oil spills all the time.

Amanda: And, as a punishment for being careless, those who pollute the oceans must pay large fines.

Blug: Punishment? For creating such beauty? Commander, I am beginning to think that Earth may not be the planet for us, after all.

Glug: Now, now, Blug, let us not be hasty. Remember, this planet has many other things to offer.

Marcos: Such as?

Glug: Just a moment while I take the ship a little lower, so we can focus on those horrible creatures you are working so hard to wipe out. We admire your determination to rid your planet of them.

Amanda: Why, what creatures do you mean?

Blug: Look at screen number six. Do you see those enormous, frightening beasts?

Marcos: Amanda, I think they're talking about whales!

Glug: Precisely! When we first started watching your planet, the oceans were filled with these awful creatures. If something hadn't been done about them, we never would have considered moving here.

Blug: But now, thanks to you earthlings, these frightening animals have almost disappeared. I cannot wait to congratulate your leaders on a job well done.

Amanda: Once again, I think you're missing the point. Whales are beautiful, peaceful creatures. Governments have passed laws making it illegal to kill them. And most people regret that whales were hunted in the past.

Marcos: Right! Almost everyone is in favor of saving the whales. If we're lucky, someday there will be many more whales in the oceans.

Blug: Let me make sure I understand this. Are you saying that earthlings wish to share their planet with huge creatures that occupy so much space?

Glug: What do you think, Blug? Could we live on a planet that has such frightening beasts?

Blug: I do not know. I just do not know.

Glug: I admit I'm beginning to feel a bit discouraged. Shall we take a short trip south? We can view that ugly place the earthlings are working so hard to clean up.

Amanda: That sounds more like it! What clean-up are you referring to?

Glug: Just sit back and relax. We'll be there in a minute. In the meantime, would you please explain something to me?

Marcos: Sure, if I can. What is it?

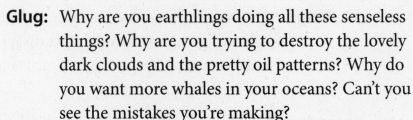

Glug: Why are you earthlings doing all these senseless things? Why are you trying to destroy the lovely dark clouds and the pretty oil patterns? Why do you want more whales in your oceans? Can't you see the mistakes you're making?

Marcos: To us, these aren't mistakes. They're things we have to do to keep our planet alive.

Amanda: Marcos is right. We're learning that every animal and every plant adds something to the environment. If one of them disappears, the environment suffers.

Blug: Do you mean to say earthlings worry more about the environment than their own pleasure?

Amanda: Well, not all of us, at least not yet. But more and more of us realize that without a healthy environment, the whole world will be sick.

Glug: Excuse me, but we're here. Look at screen number one. There's that terrible place I mentioned before. We're so grateful to you earthlings for destroying it.

Marcos: Amanda, look! We're flying over a rain forest.

Blug: So, it is called a rain forest, is it? The sight of it makes my skin crawl. All those trees and plants— the words alone make my eyes water!

Amanda: Make your eyes water? But why?

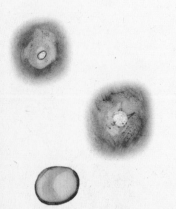

Glug: The pollen in plants makes us miserable. Fargonians are allergic to pollen. We want to come here because you earthlings are doing such a good job of destroying the plants on your planet. That will mean no more pollen some day.

Marcos: But you're wrong, Commander Glug.

Glug: What do you mean? We've been watching for a long time now. We've seen earthlings come into a—what do you call it?—a rain forest and cut down acres and acres of trees at a time. We've seen miles of plants destroyed in a matter of hours. We can tell that you people are on the right track.

Blug: Yes, yes! You have the right idea!

Amanda: No, I'm afraid that isn't the right idea. A long time ago, most people didn't know how much damage they were doing to the planet by cutting down those forests. Now we do know. And we're trying to stop it.

Glug: You mean all these trees and plants might survive? They won't be destroyed after all?

Marcos: Let's hope not! You know, the kids in our school are raising money to buy parts of the rain forest, so that it doesn't get destroyed.

Blug: This trip has certainly turned out to be a terrible disappointment. Not to mention a thousand years of traveling time wasted.

Glug: Let's take Marcos and Amanda back to where we found them, Blug. Then we had better return home with our report.

Blug: Our commander in chief is certainly going to be distressed about all this.

Glug: Why can't you earthlings just continue what you have been doing so well? In a short time, you would have the perfect planet—one that Fargonians would love.

Amanda: Maybe so. But it would be a planet none of us could live on. It would be a planet with a dead environment.

Marcos: That's right. In other words, it wouldn't be home.

Glug: You do realize that now we'll never be able to bring you all those nice things we had in mind for Earth.

Blug: No intergalactic space travel. No teleportation. No mind reading.

Amanda: I feel kind of sad about that. But you wouldn't want us to destroy our home, would you?

Glug: I suppose not. You earthlings must do what's best for your own planet. But if you ever change your minds, just leave beautiful piles of litter and lovely dark clouds and wevver shoms and . . .

Blug: And get rid of those whales!

Marcos: Somehow I don't think that will ever happen.

Glug: Well, if it does, we'll be back.

Blug: Here we are over the park. We're right back where we started—in more ways than one.

Marcos: This has been an exciting ride. Thanks.

Glug: You're welcome. I'm sorry we won't be seeing you again.

Amanda: I am, too. . . . Well, kind of. But I'm not sorry that we're trying to stop ruining the earth.

Glug: To thank you for helping us avoid a big mistake, we're going to give you a going-away present. Stand under that light over there, and we will teleport you back to the park.

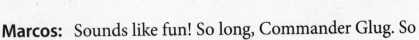

Marcos: Sounds like fun! So long, Commander Glug. So long, First Officer Blug.

Blug: Good-bye.

Glug: It's been a pleasure to meet you.

Amanda: It's been—ummmm—interesting meeting you. I hope you find another planet you can live on. Good-bye!

Marcos: Look, Amanda, we're standing exactly where we were when the ship first appeared. We've been teleported!

Amanda: Say! Where did they go? Where's the spaceship?

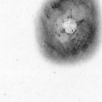

Marcos: Look up! There it is. It's almost out of sight. You know, Amanda, I just had an idea.

Amanda: What is it?

Marcos: Since the Fargonians are so fond of litter, we should have told them to get in touch with the mayor. Perhaps we could have exchanged some of our litter for a teleporter and a spaceship or two.

Amanda: That's a great idea, but they're probably making a left turn at Saturn by now. Well, what should we do next?

Marcos: I know what I'm going to do. I'm heading for the recycling center. I think it's time I got started doing something about the environment.

Amanda: Wait! I'm with you!

Name That Character!

by Gail Tuchman

Stuart Little?

CAST:
Lauren
Andrew
Beatriz
Goody Goodshow
Mystery Guests One, Two, Three, Four, and Five

SETTING:
TV Game Show Studio

Pinocchio?

Thumbelina?

Lauren: It's thirty seconds to show time, and Goody's still not here.

Andrew: Don't worry. He'll show up. He always does.

Beatriz: But why does he always have to cut it so close? Ready or not, we have to begin the countdown!

All: 10...9...8...7...6...5...4...3...2...1...

Lauren: And now, for better or for worse, and better late than never...

All: Here's... Goody!

Goody: Hello there, TV audience. And a special hello to all of you right here in our studio. Welcome to your favorite TV game show—Name That Character! I'm your host, Goody Goodshow. And what a good show this is!

All: Yay!!!

Goody: Now, here's how we play. Today you'll meet several mystery guests who are famous storybook characters. Our panel of experts will ask questions to try to identify each character. All of you sitting at home or in the studio audience can play, too. Just record your guess on a card or slip of paper. Join our panelists as they see if they can...

All: Name That Character!

Goody: Ready, Lauren? Andrew? Beatriz?

Panel: We're ready, Goody.

Goody: Oh, goody! Let's play... Name That Character! And now, let's meet Mystery Guest Number One. May we have the first question, please?

Beatriz: Welcome to Name That Character! How are you today?

Guest One: Oh, not very good. In fact, I have a feeling that this is going to be a terrible day!

Lauren: A terrible day? Why would you say a thing like that?

Guest One: When my alarm clock went off this morning, it was so loud and I was so sleepy that I thought it was the smoke detector. I yelled FIRE! FIRE! And my family and I raced over to our neighbor's house to call the fire department.

Andrew: What happened next?

Guest One: A few minutes later, the firefighters came, and they had to break a window to get into the house because the door was locked. Then they discovered it was a false alarm. At that moment, I knew it was going to be a horrible day!

Andrew: Well, that's not a great start, but is that the only reason you think it's going to be a horrible day?

Guest One: Oh, no. After the false alarm, I really had to hurry so I wouldn't be late for this show. Mom packed my breakfast so I could eat in the car. But I couldn't find my thermos, so I poured my orange juice in a cup. Well, when Dad hit a big bump, my orange juice splashed all over his briefcase—which just happened to be open. I don't think all his papers got ruined. There was at least one he could still read. Sort of. As I said, this is turning out to be a no-good day.

Goody: Let's get on with the questions, shall we?

Beatriz: Nothing else happened, did it?

Guest One: Well, I didn't see the big mud puddle outside the studio door. That is, not until I was lying in it. That was after I tripped over the skateboard, which I didn't see, either. Yes, it's been a very bad day.

Lauren: It sounds like you need a nice long rest in the country.

Guest One: I think I'd rather move to Australia!

Beatriz: Australia? Did you just say "Australia"?

Andrew: Did I hear you say "terrible day"?

Lauren: And didn't you mention "horrible, no good, very bad day"?

Panel: Gong! Gong! Gong!

Beatriz: We've got it!

Goody: Panel, can you identify our first mystery guest?

Andrew: Yes, he has to be Alexander from *Alexander and the Terrible, Horrible, No Good, Very Bad Day!*

Goody: Good guessing! Thank you, Mystery Guest Number One. Now let's give a warm welcome to our second mystery guest!

Beatriz: Tell us, Mystery Guest Number Two, where do you spend most of your time?

Guest Two: I hang out in a barn.

Lauren: Are you a horse?

Guest Two: No.

Andrew: A cow?

Guest Two: No.

Beatriz: A goose?

Guest Two: No, I'm not a horse or a cow or a goose.

Lauren: Hmmm . . . . Would you please name something that you like to do?

Guest Two: I like to go for a spin.

Beatriz: Ah, then you must be a skater.

Guest Two: No, I'm not.

Andrew: Maybe you mean going for a spin on your bike. I like to go for a spin on mine. Wait a minute! You could be a mouse. Mice hang around in barns. And there's a mouse I'm thinking of that likes to go for a spin on his bike. Well, it's a kind of bike—a motorcycle. You must be that mouse!

Panel: Gong! Gong! Gong!

Andrew: Our guess is Ralph, the mouse, from *The Mouse and the Motorcycle*.

Goody: Well, panel, you're 100 percent . . . WRONG! But you can try again.

Beatriz: Would you please name something that you are particularly good at doing?

Guest Two: I'm an expert at catching flies. In fact, I've caught thousands of flies in my day.

Lauren: Someone who catches flies has to be a baseball player. You must be a famous storybook baseball player like . . . hmmmm . . . I can't think of any. Do you play right field, left field, or center field?

Guest Two: I've never played baseball in my life.

Andrew: Well, can you tell us something about your friends?

Guest Two: Certainly! My best friend is some pig.

Beatriz: My goodness! What an awful thing to say about your best friend!

Andrew: Well, I know what our mystery guest means. My best friend slurps spaghetti all the time.

Lauren: And my best friend likes to "pig out." Tell us a little more about your friend.

Guest Two: My friend is terrific! radiant! humble! In fact, I've written letters about my friend. You see, there's a pen in the barn.

Lauren: Oh, so you're a writer. A barn is a good place for a writer to hang out. You can go up to the hayloft where you won't be disturbed. I'm sort of a writer, too. I write postcards when I go to interesting places. Have you ever been to an interesting place?

Guest Two: I went to the county fair with my friend.

Andrew: Did you write anything at the fair?

Guest Two: I wrote about my friend. But I'm not really a writer.

Beatriz: You're not a horse or a cow or a goose or a mouse. You're not a skater or a baseball player or a writer. I give up! This is just one big tangled web of mystery!

Lauren: Wait! A web! A web of mystery. That's it!

Panel: Gong! Gong! Gong!

Goody: What is your guess, panel?

Lauren: The word web made it all clear. You're Charlotte, the spider from *Charlotte's Web*, and your best friend is Wilbur, the pig.

Goody: Well, panel, this time you're 100 percent . . . RIGHT! Thank you, Charlotte. Now let's meet our third mystery guest. We're ready for your questions, panel.

Andrew: You don't by any chance live in a barn, do you?

Panel: Gong! Gong! Gong!

Guest Three: Oh, no, I live in a little house, but we've got a barn out back and a nice little cow.

Beatriz: This is a snap! You're Laura Ingalls, and you live in a little house on the prairie.

Goody: Sorry, panel, you're wrong, but I can understand why!

Guest Three: Dear me. I suppose I'd really better tell the truth. I hope you won't be angry with me for making up the part about the barn and the cow. Please say you forgive me. You see, I like to imagine things and make up stories. Once when I was . . .

Lauren: Excuse me, but that imagination of yours rings a bell. Could you tell us what you look like?

Guest Three: Why not? I have lots of freckles and bright red hair. Some people say it's the color of carrots, but I think . . .

Panel: Gong! Gong! Gong!

Lauren: That red hair is a sure giveaway! You're Anne of Green Gables, right?

Goody: Wrong! This isn't as easy as you think. Try again, panel.

Beatriz: I think we need some more clues. Tell me, Mystery Guest, do you have any unusual friends?

Guest Three: I certainly do. I have a monkey as a friend.

Andrew: Aha! Does your monkey sometimes wear a little hat?

Guest Three: Of course he does. You don't think I'd let him catch cold, do you?

© Macmillan/McGraw-Hill

Lauren: Well, that little monkey sounds like one of my favorite storybook characters. Could he possibly be Curious George?

Guest Three: Curious George? No. While my monkey is very curious, that isn't his name. My father gave him to me. He rides on my shoulder, and he's a very polite little fellow. Except for one time when I went to a picnic, and . . .

Goody: Excuse me, Mystery Guest. Maybe we'd better get on with the questions.

Guest Three: Oh, please do. Don't let me stop you.

Beatriz: Do you have any other animal friends?

Guest Three: Certainly. I have a horse, but he's more than a friend. He's almost a member of the family. He lives with me.

Lauren: Hold on. A few minutes ago, you said you made up the part about having a barn. Do you mean your horse actually lives in your house, or are you making that up, too?

Guest Three: Well, you see, my horse doesn't actually live in my house. But he does live on the porch. I wouldn't mind having him in the house, but he doesn't like the parlor. Oh—and sometimes I carry him around.

Andrew: Now I'm sure you're stretching the truth! Do you mean to tell us that you can actually lift your horse?

Guest Three: Sure! I'm very strong, you know. Once, at the circus, I won a wrestling match against the world's strongest man. Honest! You should have seen the face of the ringmaster when I . . .

Beatriz: I think I've finally got it this time! Do you wear shoes that are two times as long as your feet?

Guest Three: Absolutely! I've got to have room to wiggle my toes, don't I?

Lauren: Are you a Thing-finder?

Andrew: And did you once find a splink outside your house?

Beatriz: And is your house called the Villa Villekulla?

Guest Three: Yes, yes, and yes again!

Panel: Gong! Gong! Gong!

Goody: Good luck, panel!

Panel: You've got to be Pippi! Pippi Longstocking!

Goody: Whew! Good for you, panel! Pippi Longstocking it is. Thank you, Pippi! Now, would everyone please welcome our fourth mystery guest.

Lauren: I take it you're not a spider, a pig, or a horse—and that you don't have red braids.

Guest Four: You're right about all that, but I do have something in common with two of the other guests. Like Alexander, I know my day is going to turn out to be terrible. And, like Charlotte, I'm good at spinning.

Beatriz: Do you spin webs?

Guest Four: No, but I can spin one thing into another.

Beatriz: You're spinning this into another web of mystery. I don't know what you mean. Could you give us another clue?

Guest Four: Yes. I have a most unusual name.

© Macmillan/McGraw-Hill

Lauren: Did you say an unusual name? Hmmm . . . .
Could it possibly be Encyclopedia Brown?

Guest Four: No, that's not my name.

Andrew: Is it Rapunzel?

Guest Four: No, Rapunzel is not my name.

Andrew: Is it Thumbelina?

Beatriz: Mudge?

Lauren: Fudge?

Guest Four: No, no, and no.

Andrew: Maybe it's a name that's even more unusual. Is it Nate the Great?

Guest Four: No. Although I'm great, my name's not Nate.

Guest One: Is it Chicken Little?

Guest Two: Or Barney Bipple?

Guest Four: No to both.

Guest Three: Is it Lyle Lyle Crocodile?

Lauren: How about Tom Thumb?

Beatriz: Is it Tweedledee or Tweedledum?

Guest Four: No. No. No. Not one of those is my name!

Andrew: Is it Pinocchio?

Lauren: Is it Mrs. Piggle Wiggle?

Beatriz: Is it Stuart Little?

Guest Four: No. No! NO!!!

Goody: Panel, I'll let you have one more try.

Guest Four: Today do I brew, Tomorrow I bake, The day after
that The queen's child I'll take. Lucky I'll go As
lucky I came, For La-La-La-La Is my name!

Name That Character! 155

Lauren: Listen. Did you hear that?

Andrew: Did we ever!

Beatriz: Baking . . . brewing . . . the queen's child!

Panel: Gong! Gong! Gong!

Beatriz: Tell us . . .

Andrew: could your name . . .

Lauren: possibly be . . .

Panel: RUMPELSTILTSKIN?

Guest Four: Who told you? How did you figure it out? STAMP! STAMP! STAMP!

Goody: Don't be so angry! It's only a game. And if you don't stop stamping, you'll fall right through the floor!

Guest Four: STAMP! STAMP!

All: Crash! Bang!

Guest Four: HELP! How did I end up in the basement?

Guest One: I can see that someone else is having a terrible, horrible, no good, very bad day.

Goody: Oops! Well, it's time for a station break, anyway! Please stay tuned, and we'll be back in a moment with Name That Character! Listen, panel, I'm going to check on Rumpelstiltskin. Why don't you all just chat with our last mystery guest until I get back? Make her feel right at home.

Guest Five: Oh, don't worry about me, Goody. I'll just read through this list of suggestions you gave me before the show.

Goody: Great! Remember, everyone, the show must go on! I'll be back in a few minutes.

Guest Five: Now, let me see what Goody wrote. Look up at the panel and remember to speak up. Well, all right, but I wonder how Goody expects me to look at the panel if I'm talking to the ceiling.

Lauren: Psst, Andrew. What a character. This guest is a real joker!

Andrew: You're not kidding. She's got the entire studio audience in stitches.

Guest Five: I suppose I should take a peek at Hint #2. When the questions begin, let Beatriz get the ball rolling. Oh, how lucky it is that I just happen to have my bowling ball with me! After all, you never know when someone might say, "Have a ball!" or "Keep your eye on the ball!" Here you are, Beatriz. Just hold on to that ball until Goody gets back. Then roll it to Lauren.

Beatriz: OK, but I don't think this is quite what Goody had in mind.

Guest Five: Let's go on with Goody's list. Don't give anything away. Oh, what a shame. Just think, I baked all these delicious blueberry pies to hand out at the end of the show. That's too bad. Well, I'm sure that Goody knows best.

Lauren: Hmmm. This mystery guest is beginning to sound a lot like a character I know.

Guest Five: And here's the last of Goody's suggestions. That's easy. Let's see, I know I have a fan somewhere in my pocketbook. Yes, here it is! Ah-h-h, what a delightful breeze. I certainly feel very cool now!

Panel: GOODY! We're all waiting.

Goody: All right. Rumpelstiltskin is just fine now, and the station break is almost over. Is everyone ready to continue?

All: YES!

Goody: Welcome back to Name That Character! Panel, are you ready to ask our last mystery guest some questions?

Panel: Gong! Gong! Gong!

Guest Five: But you haven't asked me a single question!

Panel: We don't need to!

Goody: You don't? Very well, what is your guess?

Andrew: We don't need to guess.

Beatriz: We know.

Lauren: It's Amelia Bedelia, that's who!

Goody: That's right! What an amazing panel! And now I see our time is up. This is Goody Goodshow reminding you that Alexander, Charlotte, Pippi, Rumpelstiltskin, and Amelia Bedelia are all waiting for you at your local library. I'll see you next week for your favorite game show . . .

All: Name That Character!

Weather . . . whether you like it or not

by Kathleen M. Fischer

CAST:
Sound Effects Operator
Announcer
Mrs. Carlson
Febold Feboldson
Mrs. Feboldson
Mr. Parker
Paul Bunyan
Eldad Johnson
Mrs. Olson

SETTING:
Nebraska, 1860s

© Macmillan/McGraw-Hill

SOUND EFFECTS: [hail, wind, rain]

Announcer: Just listen to all those weather sounds! There's nothing as unpredictable as weather. And in the United States there is no better place for unpredictable weather than the Great Plains. Why, in those wide open spaces, there aren't any mountains or trees to stop whatever the weather is up to. And out there, the weather can be up to plenty!

SOUND EFFECTS: [hail, wind, rain]

Announcer: More than one hundred years ago, many great minds set themselves to studying science. Now about that time, a great natural scientist by the name of Febold Feboldson lived out in Nebraska. He had come to Nebraska by way of Sweden and had built himself a cabin by the Dismal River. As a scientist, Febold had more ideas than Nebraska had ears of corn.

SOUND EFFECTS: [hail, wind, rain]

Announcer: Febold didn't study any of the regular sciences like biology or chemistry. No, sir, he figured they were too easy. Instead, Febold took on a real challenge—he decided to do something about the weather. So pull up a chair and give a listen to this story that tells how Febold solved the Problem of the Great Heat.

SOUND EFFECTS: [telegraph keys]

Mrs. Carlson: This telegram sounds urgent. I'd better drop everything and rush it out to the Feboldson place right away.

SOUND EFFECTS: [hoofbeats followed by knock, knock]

Febold: Now, who could that be?

Mrs. Feboldson: Why, it's Mrs. Carlson, the telegraph operator from town.

Febold: Hello there, Mrs. Carlson. What brings you all the way out here?

Mrs. Carlson: I've got an urgent telegram for you, Febold.

Febold: Thanks very much, Mrs. Carlson. You look plumb exhausted. Why don't you sit down and rest a spell?

Mrs. Feboldson: May I offer you a glass of my ice-cold lemonade?

Mrs. Carlson: That's mighty kind of you, but I've got to get back to my telegraph office right away. So long.

Mrs. Feboldson: Land sakes, Febold! A telegram! What does it say?

Febold: Well, let's just have a look, shall we?

SOUND EFFECTS: [envelope being torn open]

Febold: Why, it's from my old boss, Paul Bunyan! Seems like he's got a terrible problem with the weather. Just listen to this:

Paul Bunyan: Dear Febold STOP Need your help immediately STOP Snow won't let up

STOP It's now July STOP Trees buried STOP Lumberjacks threatening to quit STOP Desperate STOP Contact me at Blizzard Creek Camp STOP Your friend, Paul Bunyan STOP

Mrs. Feboldson: It's still snowing in July up at Blizzard Creek! He really is in trouble, Febold.

Febold: It sure sounds as if Paul needs some help. This puts me in mind of the Year the Snow Wouldn't Melt. Remember, I solved that problem by loading up some wagons with sand from Death Valley. Then I spread all that hot sand on the snow. It was hard to believe just how fast that white stuff disappeared!

Mrs. Feboldson: That was a first-rate idea, Febold. Why don't you telegraph Paul with instructions on how to mail-order some sand from Death Valley?

Febold: First of all, it would take weeks for the sand to get from Death Valley to Blizzard Creek. Second of all, it's already July, and Paul doesn't have much time. Third of all, I already tried that solution once. A new problem calls for a new solution. Now, let me see. . . .

Mrs. Feboldson: Well, you just sit out here on the porch and think a spell. I know you'll come up with something.

Announcer: So Febold sat on the porch all afternoon and all night. At sunrise, he snapped his fingers.

SOUND EFFECTS:	[finger snap]
Febold:	Eureka! That's it! I've got it!
Announcer:	He threw a saddle on his horse, Weathervane, and galloped into town.
SOUND EFFECTS:	[hoofbeats followed by knock, knock]
Febold:	Mrs. Carlson! Mrs. Carlson! Are you up yet? It's me, Febold Feboldson!
Mrs. Carlson:	I'm just opening for the day, Febold. What's the problem?
Febold:	I don't have a problem. I've got a solution! This is urgent. I need to send a telegram to Paul Bunyan at Blizzard Creek, immediately!
Mrs. Carlson:	Hold your horses, Febold. Just write your message on this form, and I'll send it right away.
Febold:	Okay, here goes: Dear Paul STOP Your problem is the North Wind STOP It doesn't know that winter is over STOP Here's what you must do STOP Turn all your thermometers upside down STOP When the North Wind sees how "high" the mercury is, it will realize that it is summer and leave you alone STOP Your friend, Febold Feboldson STOP P.S. Next winter, don't camp at Blizzard Creek STOP
Announcer:	About three weeks later—on one of the hottest days of August—Mr. Parker, the letter carrier, was delivering the mail.

SOUND EFFECTS: [hoofbeats]

Mr. Parker: Whew, it's as hot as blazes! My next stop is the Feboldson place. Let's see if I've got all Febold's mail. Here's the newspaper and a letter from Mrs. Feboldson's sister in St. Louis.

SOUND EFFECTS: [rustling paper]

Mr. Parker: And what's this? It's a mighty big postcard for Febold. Now, that's interesting. The return address says it's from a Paul Bunyan. Could that be *the* Paul Bunyan? Maybe that's why the postcard is so large. Since it's a postcard, it wouldn't hurt to take a tiny peek. Let's just see what he says.

Paul Bunyan: Dear Febold,

Thanks for all your good advice. I can't tell you how awful things were around here. The snow was so high that we had to tunnel down to cut the trees. Then we'd yell TIMBER like always, but the trees couldn't fall because the snow held them up! You can imagine how upsetting this was for the lumberjacks.

Just as you predicted, once the North Wind saw those upside-down thermometers, it blew right back up to the North Pole. Since then, the snow has melted. Please give my best wishes to your wife.

Your friend and former boss,
Paul Bunyan

© Macmillan/McGraw-Hill

Announcer: Just then the mail wagon pulled up to the Feboldsons' gate. Mrs. Feboldson was sitting on the porch sipping lemonade with a neighbor, Eldad Johnson.

Mr. Parker: Morning, folks. Mrs. Feboldson, here's your mail.

Mrs. Feboldson: Thank you kindly, Mr. Parker. May I offer you a big glass of my ice-cold lemonade?

Mr. Parker: Thanks, Mrs. Feboldson. I'd like to take a rain check on that lemonade, if you don't mind. I need to finish making my deliveries and get back to the post office.

Eldad Johnson: I'd sure like to catch a ride back to town if you've got room in the mail wagon.

Mr. Parker: I'd be glad to have the company.

Eldad Johnson: Good-bye, Mrs. Feboldson. Thanks for the lemonade.

Mr. Parker: Good-bye, Ma'am. See you tomorrow.

Mrs. Feboldson: Good-bye, gentlemen. Try to stay cool.

SOUND EFFECTS: [hoofbeats]

Eldad Johnson: This is sure some weather we've been having. Hot enough for you?

Mr. Parker: Hot enough and then some!

Eldad Johnson: I was just talking to Febold. Word is that folks are calling this the Year of the Great Heat.

Mr. Parker: Febold's right. Nebraska's never been hotter. I just wish he'd do something about this weather.

Eldad Johnson: What do you mean—you wish he'd do something about it?

Mr. Parker: Well, you know I'm not the nosy sort. But sometimes a letter carrier can't help but notice what gets written on the back of a postcard.

Eldad Johnson: I reckon that's true. But what does that have to do with the heat?

Mr. Parker: Just this. Your neighbor Febold just happens to be a certified weather genius! He just solved a big weather problem for none other than Paul Bunyan. So there!

Eldad Johnson: *The* Paul Bunyan?

Mr. Parker: Yup. The very same!

Eldad Johnson: Febold once told me that he used to work for Paul, so I guess it's possible. What did Febold do?

Mr. Parker: He solved the weather problem Paul was having at his lumber camp. That's all.

Eldad Johnson: Parker, turn this wagon around right now. We're heading back to the Feboldson place.

SOUND EFFECTS: [hoofbeats]

Announcer: A few minutes later, the two men were standing back on the Feboldsons' front porch.

Mrs. Feboldson: Goodness! I didn't expect to see you again so soon. What brings you back in such a hurry?

Febold: Welcome, fellows. What can we do for you?

Eldad Johnson: Well, Febold—Mr. Parker, here, has been telling me that you're a certified weather genius. With this terrible heat we've been having, we sure could use a weather genius to turn things around.

Febold: Well, I'll grant you it's been a mite warm around these parts lately.

Mr. Parker: A mite? It's so hot that I'm almost out of the letter-delivering business.

Mrs. Feboldson: Why, Mr. Parker, what do you mean?

Mr. Parker: Just this. When people in these parts try to write a letter, the heat dries up the ink and blows it away before they can finish a sentence!

Eldad Johnson: He's not kidding. Why, only this morning, the mercury shot out of the top of my thermometer like a fountain. Febold, this is getting serious.

Febold: You've convinced me. I guess it's time for me to sit a spell in my thinking chair.

Mr. Parker: Febold, this is no time for sitting! It's time for doing something!

Mrs. Feboldson: Now calm down, Mr. Parker. If you want a solution to this heat, you need to let Febold sit and think about the problem. All great geniuses need time to think.

Mr. Parker: Well, all right. But how long will it take?

Febold: Why don't you two come back tomorrow? By then, I should have a plan.

Eldad Johnson: Tomorrow it is. Good-bye, Febold.

Mr. Parker: And good day to you, Mrs. Feboldson.

Febold and Mrs. Feboldson: Good-bye, gentlemen.

Announcer: So Eldad Johnson and Mr. Parker climbed back in the mail wagon and disappeared down the hot, dusty road.

SOUND EFFECTS: [hoofbeats]

Announcer: The next morning, Mrs. Feboldson stepped out to the porch, where Febold was still sitting in his thinking chair.

SOUND EFFECTS: [rooster crowing]

Mrs. Feboldson: Morning, Febold. I think I see the mail wagon coming up the road. Have you had time to think of a solution?

Febold: Yes, I do have a solution. I'm going into town to order some fog-cutters right now!

Mrs. Feboldson: Fog-cutters? Whatever for?

Announcer: Before Febold could answer his wife's question, Mr. Parker and Eldad pulled up in the mail wagon.

SOUND EFFECTS: [hoofbeats]

Mr. Parker: Whoa, there!

Eldad Johnson: Morning, Febold. I see you're still sitting in your thinking chair.

Mr. Parker: Has that chair helped you think up a way to get rid of this heat?

Febold: Now, Parker, don't go making fun of my thinking chair. As a matter of fact, I have thought of a solution.

Mr. Parker: Glory be! What is it?

Eldad Johnson: What can we do to help?

Mr. Parker: When do we start?

Febold: Hold your horses, gentlemen! These scientific solutions take a little time. First, we need to ride into town and send a telegram. Then, we'll stop at Olson's Emporium and order a pair of fog-cutters.

Eldad Johnson: Did you say fog-cutters?

Mr. Parker: What on earth are fog-cutters?

Mrs. Feboldson: You were about to explain this fog-cutter business to me when these gentlemen drove up.

Febold: Why, fog-cutters are just what they say they are! They're contraptions used to cut fog.

Mrs. Feboldson, Eldad, Parker: What fog?

Febold: Just you wait and see.

Announcer: With that, they all climbed into the mail wagon and headed into town.

SOUND EFFECTS: [hoofbeats]

Announcer: Their first stop was the telegraph office.

Mrs. Carlson:	Good morning, Febold. Gracious, it's hot. The temperature hasn't been below 125 degrees all week. I think we may even break that record today.
Febold:	Is it too hot to send a telegram?
Mrs. Carlson:	No, as far as I know, the telegraph lines haven't melted yet.
Febold:	Good. Please send this right away to Pecos Bill at the IXL Ranch in Texas.
	Dear Bill STOP I need a favor STOP Please start a stampede now STOP The more dust the better STOP Your friend, Febold Feboldson STOP
SOUND EFFECTS:	[telegraph keys]
Mrs. Carlson:	There, Febold. Your telegram has been sent. Bill should get your message soon.
Febold:	Thanks, Mrs. Carlson.
Mr. Parker:	Do you really know Pecos Bill?
Febold:	Sure, Bill and I used to work for Paul Bunyan.
Eldad Johnson:	Why did you ask Bill to start a stampede? I thought stampedes were dangerous.
Febold:	Stampedes can be dangerous, Eldad, but there's never been anyone like Bill for knowing how to handle animals. Bill's cattle will be just fine. We need that dust storm to help end the Great Heat.
Mrs. Feboldson:	Febold, don't I recollect your saying something about ordering fog-cutters?

Febold: Of course! Let's high-tail it over to Olson's Emporium and order them right now.

SOUND EFFECTS: [door opening as shop bell rings]

Mrs. Olson: Sakes alive! I didn't expect customers today. I figured everybody would stay out of the sun in this heat.

Eldad Johnson: It's on account of the heat that we're here.

Mrs. Olson: Excuse me?

Mr. Parker: Febold is a certified weather genius, and he's going to get rid of the heat.

Mrs. Olson: Do tell. Is there anything I can do to help?

Febold: Yes, there is, Mrs. Olson. I want you to order the best fog-cutters you can get.

Mrs. Olson: Now where would I get a thing like that?

Febold: Send to London, England. Everybody knows they have fog to beat the band in London. Oh, and have those fog-cutters sent special delivery. We're going to need them and fast!

Mrs. Olson: I'll send your order out today, but what do you want with fog-cutters? We've got terrible heat, not fog.

Febold: Just you wait and see.

Announcer: A few days later, Mrs. Olson and Mrs. Carlson met on the sidewalk.

Mrs. Olson: Just look at all those dark storm clouds rolling in! It feels 20 degrees cooler already.

Mrs. Carlson: Yes, indeedy, it's a lot cooler with the sun behind all those clouds. It certainly looks like rain!

Announcer: Well, those dark storm clouds were really clouds of dust kicked up by Pecos Bill's stampede. Of course, when the real clouds in the sky saw those dark clouds, they were fooled into thinking that a genuine storm was brewing. So they rushed over and started in raining as hard as they could.

Eldad Johnson: I can see the rain coming out of those clouds. But there's no rain hitting the ground.

Febold: That's because the rain is running into all the hot air that's sitting on top of the prairie. When the rain hits that hot air, it turns into steam. Then the steam turns into fog, just as I knew it would.

Mrs. Feboldson: Look, Febold, all the fog is staying up in the air.

Febold: That won't last for long, my dear. Once the air cools off a bit, that fog will come bumping down to the ground lickety-split.

SOUND EFFECTS: [hoofbeats]

Mr. Parker: I surely do hope I can get this special delivery package out to the Feboldson place before I get caught in that fog. Febold sure knew what he was doing

when he ordered these fog-cutters! It just goes to show what a certified weather genius can do when he puts his mind to it.

Announcer: Well, that was the end of the Great Heat. But within hours, the fog was thick on the ground.

SOUND EFFECTS: [muffled yells]

Mrs. Feboldson: Febold, I think I hear Mr. Parker down at the gate.

Febold: Good, he's here with the fog-cutters, and not a minute too soon!

Announcer: Febold took those fog-cutters out of the package. Over the next couple of days, he cut the fog from one side of Nebraska to the other.

Mr. Parker: Say, Febold, what are you going to do with all that fog you've cut?

Febold: Well, I think I'll just lay the strips out end to end along the dirt roads in Nebraska. In a few days, the fog should seep into the ground, leaving smooth roads for horses and wagons.

Announcer: And that's exactly what Febold did. Of course, every spring some of that fog begins to seep back up and make the dirt roads in Nebraska the muddiest mess you've ever seen. . . . But that's another story!

The Baker's Neighbor

based on a Peruvian folk tale
retold by Merrily P. Hansen

CAST:
Narrator
Woman
Man
Atahualpa
Mancocapac the Baker
Mama Ocllo
Judge
Clerk of the Court

SETTING:
Lima, Peru, many hundreds of years ago

Narrator: Once, long ago in the city of Lima, Peru, there lived a hardworking baker named Mancocapac. Every night, he mixed his ingredients and kneaded his dough and baked his bread and fine pastries. Every day, he sold these delicious baked goods to the townspeople.

Woman: There's no question about it. Mancocapac the baker makes the best bread in the city of Lima.

Man: If you ask me, there's no finer bread in all of Peru!

Narrator: Mancocapac the Baker loved hard work because of the gold it brought him. You might say that he loved gold more than anything else in the world. Now, next door to Mancocapac's bakery, there lived a man named Atahualpa. Atahualpa was very different from the baker. You see, Atahualpa did not like to work night and day. This is not to say that he was lazy. Not at all. It's just that Atahualpa was the kind of man who took time to enjoy the morning sun and listen to the birds.

Atahualpa: In my opinion, there's more to life than working to make lots of gold. It's also important to enjoy the everyday pleasures that life brings.

Narrator: Each day, early in the morning, the baker would sit in his yard and count the gold pieces he had earned the day before.

Baker: Five . . . ten . . . fifteen. . . . Now let me see. . . . First I subtract the cost of the flour, the sugar, the yeast, and the spices. Next I take out the cost of the fuel for my ovens. Then I will know how much profit I made!

Narrator: For more than an hour, the baker would figure and fret and add and subtract. Soon, the sound of the clinking gold pieces would awaken the baker's next-door neighbor.

© Macmillan/McGraw-Hill

Atahualpa: Well, I hear Mancocapac the Baker counting his gold again. That means it's time for me to get up.

Narrator: Often Mama Ocllo, the baker's wife, would greet Atahualpa as he came out into his yard.

Mama Ocllo: Good morning, Atahualpa. How are you this fine day?

Atahualpa: It's a fine day indeed, Mama Ocllo. I'm feeling wonderful. As I was coming down the stairs, I could smell the delicious aroma of freshly baked bread. Why, the smell from your bakery is a feast in itself!

Narrator: The baker, however, did not take pleasure in this compliment. In fact, he had quite a different view of the situation!

Baker: A feast, indeed. Atahualpa never comes to my shop to buy my baked goods. Instead, he profits from my bakery's aromas that are carried to him by the sea breezes. Mama Ocllo, this must stop!

Mama Ocllo: Why, Mancocapac, what are you talking about?

Baker: Just look at him! There he sits in his doorway, sniffing the air. Can't you see the look of happiness on his face?

Mama Ocllo: Of course I can. Atahualpa is happy because he enjoys the delicious smell of your bread and pastries.

Baker: That is exactly my point! These aromas are the result of my costly flour, sugar, raisins, and spices. He's enjoying these smells without any charge, while I must work most of the night in order to provide them!

Mama Ocllo: I see your point, Mancocapac. But what can you do?

Baker: I'm not sure, but I will think of something.

Narrator: For several days the baker thought and thought. The more he thought, the more annoyed he became. Then suddenly, a smile lit up his face.

Baker: Why, it's clear what I must do. When customers wish to enjoy the taste of my baked goods, they pay me. Clearly, Atahualpa must pay to enjoy the smell of these same goods!

Narrator: The baker hurried over to his desk. He sat down and began writing up a bill.

Baker: Hmm . . . I must figure in the cost of supplies as well as the gold owed for my labor. . . . Let's see, he has been enjoying these smells free of charge for at least five years. . . . When I add everything up, the total comes to five hundred pieces of gold.

Narrator: A short time later, the baker stood in front of his neighbor's door.

SOUND EFFECTS: [knock, knock, knock]

Atahualpa: Good afternoon, Mancocapac. Won't you come in? Would you like a cup of coffee? I only wish I could offer you some of the delicious pastries that I see in your shop. Unfortunately, I can only afford to smell them.

Baker: Neighbor, that's just what I wish to talk with you about!

Atahualpa: I'm sorry. I'm afraid I don't understand.

Baker: Every morning for many years, I've seen you sitting in your doorway.

Atahualpa: Yes, that's very true. I like nothing better than to sit in the morning sun and smell the delicious aromas coming from your bakery.

Baker: Aha! So you admit it!

Atahualpa: Admit what, Mancocapac?

Baker: You admit enjoying the smell of my baked goods!

Atahualpa: Of course, I admit it gladly!

Baker: Well, it must stop. For as long as I can remember, I've supplied you with splendid aromas at no cost to you. Now, here's my bill. It covers the cost of producing the fine smells that you've enjoyed all these years!

Atahualpa: A bill? Let me see it.

Baker: Do you have any questions?

Atahualpa: Do I have any questions? Why, this whole thing must be a joke! You can't give me a bill for enjoying the smells that come from your bakery! That's absurd. Ha, ha, ha, ha! I've never heard anything so funny!

Narrator: Atahualpa laughed loud and long. Hearing the noise, all the other neighbors and their children came to ask what had happened. He told them the story and read aloud the baker's bill once again.

Woman: Why, that's the funniest story I've ever heard in my life!

Man: Charging someone who eats a loaf of bread is one thing. Charging someone who smells the bread is something else! Ha, ha, ha! The baker must be joking!

Narrator: Soon the whole town of Lima knew of the baker's bill for his pastry smells.

Mama Ocllo: Mancocapac, my dear, everyone is talking about the bill you gave to Atahualpa. I can hear the ladies at the town pump talking about it while they draw their water!

Baker: I know all about it, Mama Ocllo. Why, just this morning, I was on my way to the mill to buy some

flour. A little boy ran up to me and pretended to sniff my hand!

Mama Ocllo: Why would a child do a thing like that?

Baker: So he could ask me how much I wanted for the lovely smell he had just enjoyed!

Mama Ocllo: Oh dear! What are you going to do now? Perhaps you should just drop the whole matter and apologize to our neighbor.

Baker: Apologize? Never. Since he has failed to pay my bill, there is only one thing left to do.

Mama Ocllo: What is that, Mancocapac?

Baker: I shall have to take him to court! I'll go first thing in the morning and speak to the judge.

Narrator: The judge, like most of Lima's citizens, had heard the story about the baker and his bill. Nevertheless, as the laws of Peru demanded, he listened carefully while the baker told his story.

Judge: Mancocapac, this is indeed an unusual charge you wish to bring against your neighbor. I hereby order you to appear in court in one week's time.

Baker: Your Honor, I will be here.

Judge: Clerk of the Court, I order you to go to the house of Atahualpa, neighbor to Mancocapac the Baker. Tell him to come to court in one week's time.

Clerk: Yes, Your Honor.

Judge: And one more thing—tell Atahualpa that when he comes, he must bring a bag filled with one hundred gold pieces.

Narrator: When the baker heard this, he began to rub his hands with glee. He turned to Mama Ocllo with a big smile.

Baker: Mama Ocllo, did you hear what the judge ordered? Atahualpa must bring a hundred gold pieces to court! This must mean that the judge plans to rule in my favor.

Mama Ocllo: It would seem so, Mancocapac. I wonder where poor Atahualpa will find that large amount of gold.

Narrator: The news of the judge's order spread throughout Lima. The baker was happy, for in his mind, he had already begun to count the gold pieces. However, Atahualpa was looking more and more glum each day.

Woman: Keep your spirits up, Atahualpa. All your neighbors hope that the judge will rule in your favor!

Atahualpa: Thank you, my friend. But things don't look very bright for me right now. A hundred gold pieces is all the gold I have in the world. I don't know what I'll do if the judge orders me to give it to the baker.

Man: I've heard the judge is a fair man. We must hope for the best, my friend.

Narrator: A week later, both men came to court. All of their neighbors and many other citizens of Lima came, too. They all felt sorry for the jolly Atahualpa, who now looked so sad. At last, the clerk of the court announced the judge.

Clerk: Order in the court. All rise for the judge.

Judge: You may be seated. Now, let Mancocapac the Baker and Atahualpa, his neighbor, come forward.

Narrator: The two men stepped up to a big table in front of the judge's bench. They raised their right hands

© Macmillan/McGraw-Hill

and promised to tell the truth, the whole truth, and nothing but the truth.

Judge: Now, Mancocapac, I would like you to repeat your complaint against your neighbor.

Baker: Well, you see, Judge . . .

Narrator: The baker went on and on about his work. He carefully described the flour, milk, raisins, nuts, and all the other good things that went into his breads and pastries. He figured the cost of each item. Then he explained how the aromas the neighbor smelled were the result of all his work and expense.

Judge: Thank you for your clear explanation, Mancocapac. The excellence of your baked goods is known throughout Lima. Now I would like to hear from Atahualpa, your neighbor.

Narrator: The baker stepped down from the witness stand, and Atahualpa took his place.

Judge: Atahualpa, the baker says that the morning breeze brings the costly bakery aromas to your house each morning. Is this true?

Atahualpa: Yes, Your Honor. It is true.

Judge: How would you describe the aroma of the freshly baked bread and rolls? Is the smell enjoyable, or is it annoying?

Atahualpa: Your Honor, I would have to say that the smell is very enjoyable, indeed.

Baker: What did I tell you, Mama Ocllo? You can see from the questions that the judge is on my side!

Mama Ocllo: It would seem so, Mancocapac.

The Baker's Neighbor 181

Judge: Based on what you have said, Atahualpa, the baker is correct. You have enjoyed the fragrant aromas that come from his bakery. So now you must give the baker the bag with the hundred gold pieces.

Narrator: On hearing this, the baker wanted to shout with joy. He almost fell over the witness stand railing in his hurry to grab the gold. Holding the bag in his arms, he walked toward the courtroom door.

Judge: Just a moment, Mancocapac. Before you leave, I would like you to count the hundred gold pieces, one by one.

Baker: Of course, Your Honor.

Narrator: The baker thought this was kind of the judge. After all, his lazy neighbor might have tried to cheat him! He emptied the gold pieces on the big table and began to count.

Baker: One, two, three . . .

Narrator: The baker counted slowly. He enjoyed the smooth touch of each perfectly round gold piece. He loved the glint of the golden metal. He relished the heavy clink as each piece of gold dropped onto the table. It was a feast for the eyes and music for the ears of the greedy baker! At last, the gold pieces were counted. Then the baker placed them lovingly back into the bag.

Judge: Are you satisfied that all the gold pieces are there?

Baker: I am, Your Honor. And before I leave the court, I would like to thank you for your fair and wise decision.

Judge: You are welcome. Now please hand the bag back to your neighbor.

Baker: What? Give the gold pieces back to Atahualpa? What do you mean?

Narrator: The baker continued to sputter. Then the judge rose from his chair and asked those in the courtroom to stand.

Judge: The court has heard the baker's complaint against his neighbor. The court has also listened to the neighbor admit that he has enjoyed the fragrant bakery aromas brought to his door by the sea breezes. Mancocapac the Baker, your neighbor has enjoyed the smell of your pastry and bread. And as payment, you have now enjoyed seeing his gold, touching his gold, and hearing his gold! I hereby declare that this case is settled.

Narrator: At first, everyone looked at each other in surprise. Then the crowd broke into laughter and cheers as they understood the judge's wise decision. They lifted Atahualpa up on their shoulders. Then they carried him, gold and all, back to his house. From that time on, the baker counted his gold inside his house. And the jolly neighbor enjoyed the morning sun and the delicious bakery aromas more than ever before.

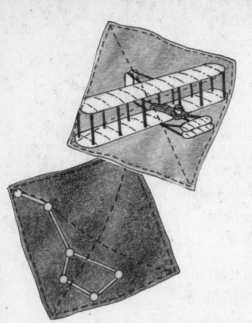
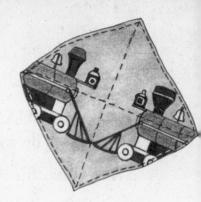

The Memory Quilt

by Claire Daniel Chapelle

CAST:

Grandfather Sullivan
Anna Sullivan
Michael Sullivan
Samantha Sullivan
Richard Sullivan
Characters of the Past
Frances Chilton
Henry Sullivan
Silas Sullivan

Alton Sullivan
Helen Sullivan
Charles Sullivan
Orville Wright
Wilbur Wright
Thomas Taylor
First Slave Hunter
Second Slave Hunter
Paul Revere

SETTINGS:

outdoor wedding—today
Kitty Hawk, North Carolina—1903
Promontory Point, Utah—1866
Lancaster, Pennsylvania—1860
Lexington, Massachusetts—1775

Grandfather: Would everyone please gather round! What a wonderful wedding celebration this is! It's a day of great joy for Thomasina and Joseph, and how happy we are to be part of it! As all of you know, one of the Sullivan family traditions is to present each newly-wed couple with a memory quilt that illustrates some of the highlights of our family history. Each square has its own very special story. On this important occasion, the four Sullivan grandchildren are going to share their favorite stories from the quilt. Are all of you ready?

Anna: Yes, Grandfather.

Michael: I think so!

Samantha: Just let me get a quick drink of water!

Richard: Ready!

Grandfather: Good! Well, then, who will begin?

Anna: I will, Grandfather! My square shows an old-fashioned flying machine. In fact, it's a picture of the very first airplane that ever flew with a motor!

Richard: I didn't think we had any ancestors who were airplane pilots.

Anna: You're right, we don't. But we did have an ancestor named Alton Sullivan who was present at the very first airplane flight.

Samantha: Did he actually meet Orville and Wilbur Wright?

Anna: He certainly did. He was only nine years old at the time! Here's my quilt story of that famous day.

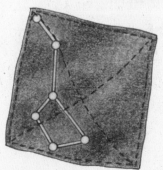

Alton: Golly, Mister Wright. I've never seen anything like this flying machine. Did you really build it?

Wilbur: We did just that, son.

Alton: But how did you ever get the idea to build a flying machine? And whose idea was it?

Wilbur: Why, both of us thought of it, son.

Orville: That's right. It wasn't all my idea, and it wasn't all his, either.

Wilbur: You see, when we were tiny sprouts, about your age, our daddy gave us a little toy that flew. It was a flying machine no bigger than your arm.

Orville: But it broke one day, and we couldn't fix it.

Wilbur: That's right. We couldn't figure out how the thing worked for the life of us. On that day, I said, "One day we will fly." Didn't I, Orville?

Orville: You sure did. And I, of course, agreed.

Alton: So now are you both famous?

Orville: Are we famous? That's a good question. Wilbur, are we famous?

Wilbur: No. Not yet, anyway. But I think we ought to tell the newspapers what we did here today. I'm sure they'll be interested.

Orville: I think you're right.

Alton: Mister Wright, why did you come to Kitty Hawk to test your flying machine?

Orville: Well, we needed a place that had lots of wind and lots of sand. You see, son, if the plane suddenly stopped and fell to the ground, the pilot could get hurt. That's why we needed soft sand to land on.

Wilbur: We knew we were talking about a beach. So we looked at the map and decided on Kitty Hawk, North Carolina. We figured it would be better here than where we live in Ohio. Too many trees there, don't you know. Besides that, Kitty Hawk gets a strong wind from the ocean. That helps the plane go faster than it would in Ohio.

Alton: But how did you know all this? Are you scientists?

Orville: No, we're not scientists. Actually, we own a bicycle shop back in Ohio.

Alton: Then how did you figure out how to build a flying machine?

Wilbur: Son, it's a long story.

Alton: Please, tell me. I really want to know. You two are my heroes.

Wilbur: We are, are we?

Orville: In that case, Wilbur, we have to tell him.

Wilbur: Well, son, after that toy flying machine broke, we tried to make others just like it. The little ones flew, but the big ones didn't.

Orville: Then we started making kites. Big kites! Our kites looked different from any kites ever made. We sure had fun trying them.

Wilbur: Then we made even bigger kites—what you call gliders. The gliders were huge flying machines that looked like this one, but they didn't have motors.

Orville: We first came to Kitty Hawk to fly those big gliders.

The Memory Quilt **187**

Alton: Because you liked the wind?

Wilbur: That's right! That was three years ago.

Alton: But today was different, right? Today you flew a flying machine with a motor for the first time! No one has ever done that before!

Orville: That's right, son. I flew 120 feet in just 12 seconds!

Wilbur: I always said we would fly one day, didn't I, Orville?

Orville: I reckon you did, brother.

Anna: And so, this square represents the first airplane flight made by Wilbur and Orville Wright on December 17, 1903, as witnessed by my great-grandfather, Alton Sullivan.

Grandfather: Very nicely told, Anna. Now, who's next?

Michael: I am, Grandfather. My favorite quilt square shows two big locomotives meeting head-on. One is going east, and the other is heading west.

Samantha: Oh! That sounds like a train crash, Michael!

Michael: No, these two trains didn't crash. They met on purpose.

Richard: That sounds pretty dangerous to me. Why would two trains ever meet on the same tracks?

Michael: Well, my quilt story explains it. You see, in 1866 there were no train tracks that went across the United States. So it was very hard for people to go to places out West, like California and Utah.

Richard: Not like today when we can go by car or bus or plane or train.

© Macmillan/McGraw-Hill

Michael: That's right. So back then, the railroad companies decided to build one track from California heading east and another track from the east heading west. The tracks met and joined in a place called Promontory Point, Utah. What a special day that was!

Samantha: That must have been hard work, tunneling through mountains and going over rivers and all.

Michael: It certainly was, and I'm proud to say that our ancestor Silas Sullivan helped build the railroad tracks that made it possible for the two trains to meet. My story begins with Silas and a fellow worker named Thomas Taylor in their tent. Remember, the year is 1866. It's just about sunset.

Silas: It surely was a hard day today.

Thomas: You said it, friend. There isn't one muscle in my body that doesn't ache.

Silas: Mine, too. I'm pretty strong, but I don't feel it today. I'm mighty tired, and my stomach feels upset. I haven't felt good for over a week.

Thomas: You aren't the first one to get sick on this crew, either. I hear tell that over a hundred workers quit last week alone. Strong, hearty men, too.

Silas: Say, have you noticed that the Chinese workers never seem to get sick?

Thomas: Yup. It doesn't make sense, either. They don't even get meat every day as we do. All they eat is fish and vegetables, boiled rice, and tea. It's the strangest thing I ever saw. We get weaker and weaker, and they get stronger and stronger.

Silas: Maybe they know something we don't.

Thomas: Could be. It sure beats me how they do it! They do the hardest jobs, too—the jobs no one else wants. They grade the hillsides and fill the huge valleys with dirt. Look at the way they lay the ties—as even as can be! They work day in and day out, and they don't ever get sick!

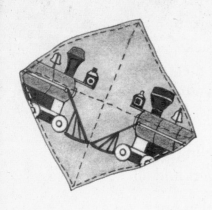

Silas: You know, I've wanted to work on this railroad ever since I first heard about it. The trains that run on these tracks will help people settle out West. But the way things are going, I'm not sure I'll be able to stick it out.

Thomas: I've been thinking about quitting myself. I hear tell that folks are getting rich digging for gold in California. We're not getting rich here—we're just getting tired and sick. If it's not a mosquito attack, it's a snowstorm. If it's not a snowstorm, it's stale beef and muddy water. I don't think I can take much more of this.

Silas: I wonder if those Chinese workers can help us.

Thomas: The Celestials? How could they help us? They stick to themselves. Most of 'em don't speak any English, either.

Silas: I don't rightly know yet, but I intend to find out. Tomorrow I hope to be a wiser man.

Michael: And so, Silas did just that! For the next week, he worked alongside the Chinese workers, called "Celestials" because they came from China, the Celestial Kingdom. He asked them questions, and he learned. He learned that boiling the water helped them to keep from getting sick. And he began to eat the boiled rice, the fish, and the

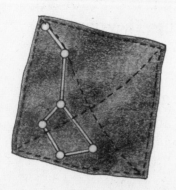

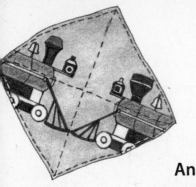

vegetables that they ate. He drank their tea instead of muddy water. Soon he became stronger and stronger.

Anna: Did he stay until all the track was laid?

Michael: He certainly did! He was there on May 10, 1869. On that day, the last spike was driven into the rails. And on that day, the two locomotives shown on this quilt square met at Promontory Point, Utah.

Richard: And what happened to his friend Thomas?

Michael: Thomas didn't believe that eating rice and vegetables was the answer. He got really sick and finally left the railroad to look for gold in California. He might have struck it rich, or he might have given up and gone back to his family in Virginia. Silas never knew what happened to him.

Grandfather: Thank you very much, Michael. You did an excellent job. Now, who will tell us the next quilt story?

Richard: I will! And it's my favorite story!

Samantha: That's an unusual picture, Richard. It looks like a design made out of stars.

Richard: It is. If you look closely, you'll see the outline of the Big Dipper. This constellation of stars was used by escaping slaves to keep them headed north, toward freedom. The Sullivan family helped slaves in the 1800s escape to freedom along the Underground Railroad.

Anna: Was it really a train that ran under the ground?

Richard: No. The Underground Railroad had no rails, engines, or railroad cars. It was the network of

roads, rivers, boats, and wagons that slaves used to travel to freedom. Its stations were the houses and churches where the escaping slaves hid along the way.

Anna: How did they get from station to station?

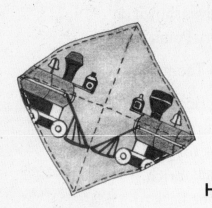

Richard: The Underground Railroad had "conductors." Conductors were former slaves or people like two of our ancestors who helped slaves in their flight to freedom. My quilt story begins on a cold winter afternoon near Lancaster, Pennsylvania. The year is 1860. Helen and Charles Sullivan, who were part of this Underground Railroad, are watching their children play in the snow.

Helen: Oh, Charles! Look outside! The children are having such a wonderful time in the snow.

Charles: That's quite a snow fort they have built. All three of them can easily fit inside.

Helen: How I long to be a child again—to be without worries or problems! They have no cares, save trying to dodge a snowball thrown by a brother or sister.

Charles: Yes, I'm afraid our cares are more serious than that. How many slaves are we hiding today?

Helen: A family of four. They arrived late last night, cold and frightened. I feared for their safety in the house, so I took them to the barn.

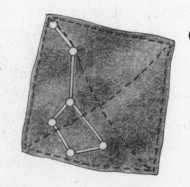

Charles: Even the barn is not safe. The slave hunters suspect us. If our house is to continue to be a station on the Underground Railroad, we will have to dig a cellar secretly. There is no other way.

Helen: How did the slave hunters discover our secret? We have been so careful!

Charles: I don't know. It could be anyone. Some of our closest neighbors believe that escaped slaves should be turned in rather than helped on their way to freedom. These people, who call themselves our friends, would turn the slaves in and see us arrested. Look there, Helen! I think I see the slave hunters coming down the lane!

Helen: What can we do? We have to save the family in the barn!

Charles: If the slave hunters find them, I will be put in jail.

Helen: No! I will not allow that to happen. I have an idea that I think will work.

Richard: Fifteen minutes pass. When we return to the Sullivan family once more, the three children are still outside playing— screaming, running, and dodging the snowballs they are throwing at one another. Suddenly a loud knock sounds at the door of the house. Helen seems calm as she opens it.

Helen: Won't you come in? What brings you gentlemen to our home?

First Slave Hunter: Mrs. Sullivan, we have word that you are hiding four slaves who escaped last week.

Charles: We believe that slavery is wrong. But you will find no slaves in our home.

Second Slave Hunter: That may be so, Mr. Sullivan. However, it's our job to search your house.

First Slave Hunter: And the barn, as well.

Helen: Very well. Do what you must.

Second Slave Hunter: Those are mighty cute children you have out there, Mrs. Sullivan. They're having themselves one fine time.

Helen: They do love to play in the snow.

Charles: Perhaps they should come in now, Helen. They have been out too long in the cold. I'll go get them.

Helen: Oh, no, Charles! Let them play just a little longer. This is the first good snow we have had all winter.

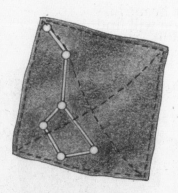

Richard: The slave hunters made a thorough search of the house and the barn. Then they returned to the house.

Second Slave Hunter: Very well. We have found nothing, inside or out. Sorry to have bothered you folks.

First Slave Hunter: Just remember it's your duty to let us know if you see anyone suspicious. The courts have ruled that a runaway slave is stolen property. So aiding runaway slaves is against the law. The punishment is harsh—six months in jail and a $1,000 fine!

Charles: So we have been told.

Richard: With that, the slave hunters left the Sullivan farm.

Samantha: But where were the runaway slaves hiding?

Anna: Why didn't the slave hunters find them when they searched the barn?

Michael: Come on, Richard. Don't keep us in suspense!

Richard: The slaves were hiding in the children's snow fort! While the slave hunters were searching the house, Mrs. Sullivan sneaked out to the barn and led the slaves to safety in the snow fort. She told the children to continue to play as if nothing unusual was happening. The children's courage saved the four slaves from capture and their parents from jail.

Grandfather: That story always brings a lump to my throat. And you did a wonderful job of telling it, Richard.

Richard: Thank you, Grandfather.

Grandfather: Now, Samantha, it looks like you have the last quilt story to share with us.

Samantha: I do. Can everybody see my quilt square?

Anna: I can. It looks like a man on a horse.

Samantha: Right. The man on this horse was not one of our ancestors, but he did play a part in our family history, as you'll see in a minute. My quilt story takes place in Lexington, Massachusetts, in 1775—a very long time ago.

Richard: That is a long time ago. It's about a hundred years before my Underground Railroad story took place.

Michael: Did you say 1775? Why, I know that date! That was the beginning of the Revolutionary War, right? The War for Independence?

Samantha: That's right. And this story starts just a few hours before the beginning of that war. Our ancestor Henry Sullivan was talking to a beautiful young lady. Her name was Frances Chilton. Now imagine them in her uncle's home. It's a little after midnight on April 19, 1775.

Frances: Henry! It is late! You must leave at once. If my uncle returns and finds you still here, he will not be happy. It is not proper to be courting a young lady at this hour!

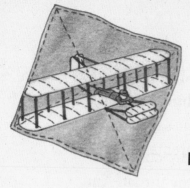

Henry: Just answer my question with a "yes." Then I will take my leave from your uncle's house as the happiest man alive.

Frances: Henry Sullivan, you are a good and kind man, but I cannot agree to marry you.

Henry: Am I not handsome enough for you, my dear lady?

Frances: Why, Henry, you know that is not the case!

Henry: Is it my income? Am I not wealthy enough?

Frances: I am not a woman to marry for money. I care little for property, servants, or silk dresses.

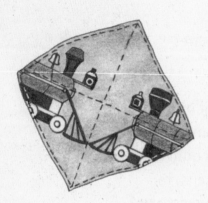

Henry: Then what is it? Do you think I do not love you enough?

Frances: I think you love me quite well.

Henry: Do you not care for me?

Frances: I care for you a great deal, and I want to be married, but . . .

Henry: But what?

Frances: Henry, these are not easy times. King George and his British soldiers are becoming more hostile to those of us in the colonies. Every day, more British troops arrive in Boston. I am afraid war will begin at any moment. Do you really think this is the best time to get married, Henry? A war will change our lives.

Henry: It is true that this is not a perfect time to get married. But if we want to be together, I think we should not postpone our wedding day.

Samantha: At that moment, Henry's proposal was interrupted by the sounds of an approaching horse. Henry and

© Macmillan/McGraw-Hill

Frances ran to the window to see a man galloping toward the house. They threw open the door to find the famous Paul Revere!

Paul Revere: The British are coming! The British are coming! You, sir, are you a minuteman?

Henry: I am, sir. I live in nearby Lincoln.

Paul Revere: Then be at the Concord Bridge at dawn! We must protect our ammunition supplies from the British. Do you have a horse?

Henry: I do.

Paul Revere: Then spread the alarm as you make your way home. Warn every family along the way that the British troops are marching to Concord. Now you must pardon my haste, but I must say good night to you!

Samantha: And so, our ancestor Henry Sullivan witnessed Paul Revere's famous ride. A short time later, Paul Revere and his companion Dr. Samuel Prescott were captured by the British. Dr. Prescott escaped and carried the message to the patriots in Concord.

Anna: And did Henry Sullivan take the message to Lincoln?

Samantha: Yes, he did. And the very next day, he fought with the Lincoln minutemen at the North Bridge in Concord. He was there when the British redcoats ran away from the patriots.

Richard: What happened to Frances and Henry? Did they ever get married?

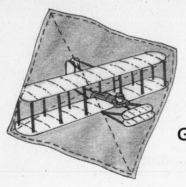

Samantha: Oh, yes. They were married the next summer, and they lived quite happily.

Grandfather: Samantha, that was an excellent story. And now, if the four grandchildren will pass the quilt along, we will present it to Joseph and Thomasina.

Anna: We welcome you, Thomasina, to the Sullivan family.

Michael: Joseph and Thomasina, we hope that you will be very happy together.

Samantha: Maybe someday you will have a story to add to this quilt.

Richard: And then, maybe someday your children will tell that story at another happy family gathering like this one!

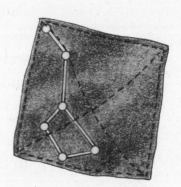

THE LION AND THE OSTRICH CHICKS

based on an African folk tale by Ashley Bryan
by Kathleen M. Fischer

CAST:
Narrator
Mama Ostrich
Papa Ostrich
Chick One
Chick Two
Chick Three
Chick Four
Chick Five
Chick Six
Lion
Mongoose
Fox
Zebra
Hare

SETTING:
Africa

Narrator: Once upon a time, Papa and Mama Ostrich got ready to have a family. Papa Ostrich made a nest in the sand for Mama Ostrich. He swooped about and scooped out a shallow nest. He smoothed over all the lumps and bumps. Then Mama Ostrich stepped in, settled down, and laid six eggs. Mama and Papa Ostrich took turns sitting on the eggs.

Mama Ostrich: I sit on the eggs by day.

Papa Ostrich: I sit on the eggs by night.

Narrator: They warmed the eggs.

Mama Ostrich: We watch.

Papa Ostrich: We wait.

Narrator: One morning, six weeks later, six little ostrich chicks kicked their way out of their shells. The parents circled around their children, scuffing their feet in the sand and singing.

Mama and Papa: Ostrich stretch, strut, stride, and race. Six little chicks just joined the chase. Clap for Ostrich, one, two! Stamp for Lion, shoo, shoo!

Narrator: Papa boomed out the news of the chicks' arrival for all to hear. His deep, lionlike roar startled the six little chicks. They ran to their mama.

Mama Ostrich: There is nothing to fear, my chicks. That deep, hissing roar is your papa's voice.

Narrator: She brought them closer to Papa. The chicks listened as he sounded his deep, hissing roar again.

Chick One: That's our papa.

Chick Two: Well, all right, Papa!

Narrator: The chicks were so excited to be in the world. They jumped into the air and fluttered their wings in flight. Down they tumbled to the ground.

Mama Ostrich: Two pretty little wings, but too tiny to fly.

Papa Ostrich: Now don't you cry. We can't fly high on our wings, but we sure can fly on our feet. Watch me!

Narrator: Papa Ostrich raced from a nearby bush to a distant tree and back.

Papa Ostrich: Uh-huh. Did you see my feet fly? We're the only two-toed birds around, and we use our feet to cover ground.

Narrator: Papa Ostrich taught the chicks his best running tricks.

Chick Three: Every day we practice our steps: stretch, strut, and stride.

Chick Four: We get better and better and run faster and faster.

Narrator: Weeks passed and soon the chicks could outrun everyone around.

Chick Five: Today we challenged Zebra and Hare and beat them by a mile!

Chick Six: We raced Deer and Fox and left them in the dust!

Narrator: The chicks were fit and fast and always finished first. They could even keep up with their parents.

Mama Ostrich: You're fast and that's fine. But don't run off too far from home, not until you're fully grown and know your way around.

All Chicks: We won't.

Narrator: One morning the chicks awoke before anyone else. They rose early to practice dashes, relays, and sprints. Now that they had learned to fly on their feet, they didn't miss wings at all.

All Chicks: Let's go!

Narrator: Away they ran, They raced from their home to a nearby bush. They rushed past the bush to a distant tree. From the tree they chased to the hill beyond. Down the hill they sped, then around a pond. They flew on their feet to a field full of rocks. They leaped and they hopped and they came to a stop.

All Chicks: Ah . . . Ah!

Narrator: They fell on the ground and rolled around. They had run so far. They felt so proud. They laughed and gasped and caught their breath.

Chicks One, Two, Three: Ah . . . Whew!

Chicks Four, Five, Six: Ah . . . Whew!

Narrator: They'd had so much fun running, they hadn't given a thought to where they were going or how far they had gone. They looked around, and they didn't recognize anything.

Chick Two: Where are we?

All Chicks: We're lost! We're lost!

Narrator: Just then a familiar, roaring sound came from behind the mound of rocks ahead.

Chicks One and Two: Papa!

Chicks Three and Four: Mama!

Chicks Five and Six: Here we are!

Narrator: They ran to the mound of rocks and peered behind. Suddenly, SHRUMP! Lion swept all six chicks into his den.

Lion: Welcome home, children.

Chick Three: You sound like Papa. But you don't look like Papa at all.

Chick Four: You're all fur, four feet, and no feathers.

Lion: I can stand on two feet, too, just like you. I'm your papa now.

Narrator: Lion tapped their stomachs.

Lion: Hmmmmm.

Narrator: Lion licked his lips.

Lion: Mmmmmm. You must be tired, my little chicks. Now go to bed.

Narrator: When their children didn't come home that day, Mama and Papa Ostrich searched everywhere. The chicks were nowhere around, nowhere to be found. The next morning Mama and Papa Ostrich set out early to ask if anyone had seen their chicks, but no one had. Finally, Mama Ostrich asked Mongoose.

Mama Ostrich: Have you seen my six chicks?

Mongoose: I was up early yesterday, and I saw them running. They ran from their house to a nearby bush. Then they ran from the bush to a distant tree.

They raced from the tree to the trail up the hill. I saw them running with all their might till they crossed the hill and dropped out of sight. Now just past the hill there's a pond below. If they circled around and didn't fall into the pond, they were bound to come to the mound of rocks where Lion lives. You don't suppose . . .

Narrator: Mama Ostrich's heart went flip-flop. She didn't wait for Mongoose to finish, and she didn't stop to think or to thank Mongoose. She rushed off, whish! past the nearby bush. She raced past the distant tree, whee! She sped on the trail up the hill beyond, and she picked up speed as she circled the pond. Then she came to the mound of rocks, whoa! She stopped. Just ahead was Lion's den. Lion sat at the entrance guarding the chicks.

Mama Ostrich: My children!

Lion: Your children? Uh-uh! My children!

Mama Ostrich: Anyone can see they're mine.

Lion: Anyone is no one. And you'll need someone to stand up to me.

Narrator: Mama Ostrich was confused by Lion's crafty talk, but she wasn't confused about whose children Lion was claiming as his own. Lion was busy teaching the chicks how to crouch and pounce like lions.

Lion: Stop that ostrich-hop. Do the lion-crouch I taught you. If you step out of line, snip! I'll snap off your heads.

You're lions now. Did you hear what I said?

Mama Ostrich: Oh! Don't mistreat them. And please don't eat them.

Lion: Uh-uh! Not now, anyway. But when they're fatter, that will be another matter. Now take off, you tall-necked, long-legged, two-toed, top-heavy bird!

Narrator: Lion bared his teeth and growled. Mama Ostrich fled for help. She found Papa Ostrich. They went together to tell their story to Chief Counselor Fox and the animal counselors. They listened and agreed to help.

Fox: A strange story, but a simple case. It's clear that no true parent could possibly mix cubs and chicks.

Papa Ostrich: Uh-uh. That's Lion's tricks, not Lion's chicks.

Mama Ostrich: Oh, look! Here comes Lion now. He's walking my chicks!

Narrator: Lion came striding by, walking upright with the six chicks in tow. The counselors bowed politely to Lion.

Lion: Meet my children.

Zebra: Nice chicks . . . er . . . children you have, Lion.

Hare: What a fine, feathered family!

Fox: Uh-huh! Note the resemblance.

Mama Ostrich: Stop him!

Papa Ostrich: Everyone knows those are our children.

Narrator: But no one dared stop Lion as he walked off with the chicks. So Mama and Papa Ostrich decided to call a meeting of all the animals. Though the counselors did nothing, Mama and Papa were sure Lion would have to listen if all the animals spoke up for them. Mama Ostrich sought out Mongoose at once. He had helped her before, and she knew he was clever.

Mama Ostrich: How could the counselors let Lion get away with this? They promised to help me get my chicks back from Lion.

Mongoose: Aha, you see it's easy for them to stand up for your rights to your face. To stand up for your rights in Lion's face is another thing.

Mama Ostrich: Well, Lion may be hardhearted, but there is a proverb: "Infinite boiling will soften the stone."

Mongoose: Uh-huh, but another proverb says: "In the court where the judge is a fox, the jury foxes, and the witnesses foxes, the goose doesn't stand a chance."

Mama Ostrich: Oh, my!

Mongoose: Let's face it: you're a bird among animals.

Mama Ostrich: What can I do? I won't give up until my children are home again.

Mongoose: Listen! Before you call all the animals together, dig a tunnel under the tall ant hill at the meeting ground.

Mama Ostrich: A tunnel? What for?

Mongoose: Don't ask, just dig. Start digging near the assembly place. Uh-huh, go to it and do it. Dig it large enough for me, but too small for Lion! Dig, dig, dig till you've dug through to the opposite side of the ant hill. Well, all right, dig, dig, dig! When it's all dug out, don't breathe a word about the tunnel to anyone. You dig? Leave the rest to me.

Narrator: Mama Ostrich dug the tunnel clear through the ant hill even though she didn't know what good it would do. Then she and Papa Ostrich called all the animals to the meeting. The animals gathered at the meeting place by the tall ant hill. Chief Counselor Fox and the other counselors sat facing the crowd.

Fox: Order, order! We have a serious matter to settle today. Mama and Papa Ostrich claim Lion has taken their children. Lion claims the children are his. To whom do you say they belong?

Narrator: The animals looked at the chicks trembling between Lion's paws. They looked at Mama and Papa Ostrich. Uh-huh, they were not fooled.

Fox: Ready to vote?

Narrator: Lion stood up on two feet.

Lion: I'll take your votes personally, one by one. You don't mind if I do, do you, Chief?

Fox: As a matter of fact, that is against the rules. But I think we can make an exception in your case, Lion.

Narrator: Lion approached the animals one by one to take each vote. He looked straight into their eyes.

Lion: Whose?

Zebra: These chicks could be cubs. Indeed, they are your children, Lion, uh-huh, uh-huh!

Lion: Whose?

Hare: These chicks walk the way you do. Indeed, they are your children, Lion, uh-huh, uh-huh!

Narrator: By the time Lion reached Mongoose, all of the animals had gone back on their promise to support Mama and Papa Ostrich. All the votes were in favor of Lion.

Lion: Well, Mongoose, let me have your vote. That will end this meeting. I'm hungry and I want to take my children home . . . to eat.

Narrator: Mama and Papa Ostrich knew just what Lion meant.

Mama and Papa: Oh, no!

Narrator: Mongoose looked straight back at Lion. He spoke loud and clear for all to hear.

Mongoose: Lion lies! We all have eyes. Lion may stand on two feet now, but he looks foolish. He is no bird! You all know the proverb: "A log may lie in the water for ten years, but it will never become a crocodile!" When has anyone ever heard that fur can beget feathers? Uh-uh! The chicks are ostriches!

Narrator: Lion stood stock still. He was stunned for the moment. And that moment was all Mongoose needed. He leaped for the tunnel and escaped down the hole.

Lion: I'll dive down the hole after you, Mongoose!

Narrator: POW! Lion fell back and rolled over. He roared in anger and tried again, but he was too large to fit through. The meeting broke up, and the animals scattered. As they ran, they chanted.

All Animals Except Lion: Fur beget feathers! Fur beget feathers! No one's ever seen fur beget feathers!

Narrator: Mama and Papa Ostrich quickly gathered their chicks, and the eight ostriches sprinted all the way home. Lion paced back and forth near the hole. He pawed and clawed at the entrance.

Lion: Come out! Come out! I'll give you "fur beget feathers"!

Narrator: Mongoose didn't hear a word of Lion's fuss over fur and feathers. He had sped right out the other end of the tunnel and kept going.

Lion: I know you're in there. You've got to come out this way, and I won't budge from here until you do. You sly old Mongoose!

Narrator: Insults didn't bring Mongoose out either. He was now safe at home. Lion finally tired of the roaring, pouncing, and clawing. He crouched down on the ground before the hole and waited for Mongoose to come out. Hours passed. Lion still sat there, too stubborn to move. He grew hungrier and hungrier.

Lion: I'll eat Mongoose when I catch him.

Narrator: Lion grew weaker and weaker.

Lion: He won't give me the slip!

Narrator: Lion grew fainter and thinner.

Lion: Where's my Mongoose dinner?

Narrator: At last, hush, he wasted away. Then Mama and Papa Ostrich stretched and strutted freely with their chicks.

Mama Ostrich: I've got a present of mangoes for Mongoose.

Six Chicks: Oh, mangoes for Mongoose! Mangoes for Mongoose!

Narrator: Mama Ostrich and her six chicks went to thank Mongoose. When Mongoose came out to meet them, the six chicks cheeped a song.

Six Chicks: Fur beget feathers, fur beget feathers. No one's ever seen fur beget feathers.

Narrator: They danced around Mongoose, singing their song. And Mama Ostrich handed Mongoose two large, juicy mangoes.

All Animals Except Lion: Clap for Ostrich, Mongoose, too!
Stamp for Lion. Shoo! Shoo!

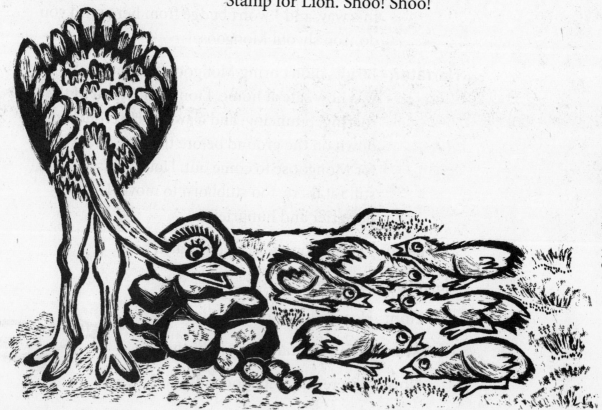

Think-Aloud
COPYING MASTERS

I wonder . . . .

I made a connection when . . .

I figured out _____ because . . .

Think-Aloud Copying Master 4 215

I thought _____ was important in this text because . . .

Think-Aloud Copying Master 7